Pot of Gold

Meriel Brooke

FARMING PRESS

First published 1997

A catalogue record for this book is
available from the British Library

ISBN 85236 409 1

Published by Farming Press
Miller Freeman plc
Wharfedale Road, Ipswich IP1 4LG, United Kingdom

Front and back cover photos by Peter Joyce

Cover design by Smart Graphics
Typeset by Galleon Typesetters, Ipswich
Printed and bound in Great Britain by
Biddles Ltd, Guildford and King's Lynn

To my father, who always wanted to be a farmer, but died before he could realise his dream

Introduction

All the world's a stage,
And all the men and women merely players;
They have their exits and their entrances,
And one man in his time plays many parts . . .

William Shakespeare

Why do a middle-aged business man and an actress decide to invade completely new territory and become farmers?

In 1991 Roger was forty-eight years old and a senior manager at IBM. He had joined the company nearly thirty years before as an engineer but transferred to sales eight years later. He was enthusiastic and ambitious: the more successful he became, the harder he worked and the more he enjoyed it. Sometimes he played squash before work, or went jogging, or did a rigorous programme of RAF exercises, but he was usually at his desk by 6 a.m.

I had trained as a nurse and worked as a surgeon's assistant for eleven years, before training as an actress, then a drama teacher, and finally becoming very interested in directing. I worked in films and television, but mainly in the theatre, including the Royal Shakespeare Theatre and the Royal National Theatre.

Neither of us knew anything about farming, it had never crossed our minds.

We had been married for nine years, had four children from previous marriages, and lived in a large detached house, with nearly a third of an acre and a swimming pool, near Barnes Common. We had two cars, one a Jaguar; were members of Roehampton Tennis Club and played there frequently; had two holidays a year; were regular visitors to the theatre and Covent Garden; and ate out at least once a week. We had some cats, and two large dogs which I walked on Wimbledon Common or in Richmond Park every day. We had a wonderful housekeeper to look after us. Life was good and we were happy.

I had just directed my third play, when something occurred which disrupted our way of life: IBM offered early retirement packages across the company. We decided that this offer was very attractive, and that if we moved to a smaller house we would have a considerable sum of money to invest. Roger was also getting frustrated in his job and was thinking of moving from IBM or starting his own company. So it all seemed to be slotting into place.

But Fate had other ideas. The recession started to bite; the sale of the house fell through; house prices started to fall. This state of affairs continued for two years. We couldn't find a house that we liked in or around London for the price we were prepared to pay and started looking further afield. Every time a sale fell through and the price of our house dropped, we turned a page of the map and looked further west. Twice we thought we had sold and twice we found a house we liked, the first time quite a large house in a village with a tennis club nearby, in Oxfordshire; the next time a smaller house with more land, in Gloucestershire.

During the two-year search for houses, country life had begun to appeal more and more. My son, Michael, had given me a book on self-sufficiency for my birthday, and Roger had become very interested in the idea. He had also decided that he would like to spend more time with me, before my ten years' head-start took me out of the race! Coincidentally, Roger had been head-hunted by two prestigious companies, and I had been short-listed for a job I dearly wanted at the Royal Shakespeare Company – but we had already set off down another road.

We suddenly had two buyers, and in the end the sale was quick. Although we had by now looked at seventy houses, we had nowhere to move to, and came back to look again in Herefordshire to find somewhere to rent while we continued the search. Elated by selling at last, we were filled with dread at the thought of a double move, and prayed that somehow, at the last moment, we would find the house of our dreams.

The first day of our final search yielded nothing,

and we were feeling despondent and exhausted. Back at our guest house that evening, the landlady gave us the housing section of the local paper. That was our first glimpse of the place that was to change our lives completely. The next morning we phoned the house agent, but they were unable to get hold of the lady who held the key. The house had come on the market that very week and they had no particulars. They told us where it was situated, and we decided to look at it anyway.

We drove up a steep narrow lane overhung with trees, like a green tunnel. At the top, rolling hills and fields appeared, and on the right an old stone wall stretched to the gate and beyond, embracing the old stone house which formed part of the walled courtyard. The other sides of the grassed courtyard were bounded by stone outhouses and a huge barn, all with stone tiled roofs. It looked serene and welcoming, mellow and beautiful in the sunshine. Ivy and lilac grew without restraint. Everything was green. I felt my heart bound and my eyes smart. We peered through the windows, but it was difficult to see anything except that the interior was old-fashioned and had no visible modern appliances. There was a lot of work to be done to make it comfortable. It didn't seem to matter. I knew this was the place. I knew we had, at last, come home.

The Beginning

Unless you try to do something beyond what you have already mastered, you will never grow.

Ralph Waldo Emerson

We moved to Upper Bridge Court in September 1993. The move was a nightmare: both removal vans broke down, one van got stuck on the hill after a tree fell on top of it, the other completely broke down trying to come to the rescue of the first, and was towed away by the local garage. We had been up at an early hour, cleaned the house, driven from London with our two cats, and had waited for several hours for the arrival of the rest of our possessions. But we were still in good spirits, and sat on a window ledge drinking a bottle of champagne, waiting for the vans to reappear.

We waited until darkness fell.

The first night was spent sleeping on the floor with no food and no furniture, not wishing to leave the house because of our two terrified cats. The removal men slept in the vans, and were given a free breakfast at the local inn. We were very hungry – but we had food for the cats!

The next day the furniture was relayed up the lanes from the broken-down vans, in a hired truck. The rain bucketed down; the paths were a sea of mud. Everyone was fed up and tempers were short. Roger and I dashed down to the inn for our first meal since leaving London.

When we returned, it was to find furniture thrown around anywhere (although everything had been previously labelled), and no boxes were unpacked. What's more, the foreman informed us that the move was going to cost us an extra 30 per cent because of the extra cost incurred to them. At this stage, unbeknown to me, Roger had a very unpleasant row with the Company office on the telephone, and was told that all our furniture would be taken back to London if we didn't pay the whole amount then and there, and our computers might get dropped in the process. Roger felt he had no choice but to pay up. The rest of our precious possessions were hurriedly unloaded, and I sat down amongst the packing cases and burst into tears.

The following morning we came downstairs and stood together in our doorway. For the first time we felt the peace. There was no roar of traffic, no rumble of trains. The removal men had gone. We were on our own. The rain had stopped, and beyond the walled courtyard the rain-washed fields rose to the skyline; above them shimmered a rainbow, curving down into the field below the house. After the rain comes the rainbow, and they say that at the foot of every rainbow is a pot of gold.

We started the daunting task of moving things into the correct rooms and unpacking the boxes which filled every available bit of space. Carpets and books had been piled into the barn, and there they were to stay for over a year. Well, the carpets are still there now, because we haven't finished lifting floor boards to do the wiring. Will the mice and rats have destroyed them when we finally bring them into the house?

We were still struggling to get things straight when Roger was called to start his farming life. We had bought 5 hectares of land, one of which was taken up by the house, garden, courtyard, and paddock, leaving two fields of about 2 hectares each. One of our neighbouring farmers, David Griffiths, had been renting the land before the house was sold, and we had agreed that he could continue to do so until we were ready to use it, as long as he put all the fences into good repair: his sheep were in one of the fields and we were worried about our two large town dogs suddenly being surrounded by sheep. David seemed equally worried and gave us sombre warnings about what would happen to dogs who chased sheep. He arrived early one morning with his fencing equipment and Roger hurried out to help.

They worked through several lovely warm autumn days, and I envied them being out there while I unpacked boxes and washed shelves. This was my first taste of the role of the country woman in the home while her man works on the land! I would take them out a drink from time to time and marvelled to see Roger's slight figure carrying huge posts and rolls of fencing wire. He learned a lot from David Griffiths, and can hang a gate or put up a fence himself now. His strength has grown with his abilities: he can now load a trailer full of 25-kilo sacks of grain and throw 15-kilo hay bales to the top of a stack. We are always amazed by the strength of the farmers, some of them quite slight in stature – they say it's a knack and have given us a few tips, but I reckon they have learned it from the cradle.

Our neighbours are the salt of the earth. David Griffiths, from down the hill, lives with his mother, and runs his whole farm single handed, and has done since his father was taken ill when he was in his teens. Richard Morgan came and knocked on our door the first Christmas we were here and introduced himself with a present of swedes that he had grown, the first of many gifts of food. He and his younger brother Brian, his father Lee and his mother Margaret, run a mixed farm of sheep and cattle, up the hill, and they have proved good friends and mentors, always ready with advice, but it is never given unless we ask for it. They never belittle us for our mistakes, but encourage us in our efforts, and give us absolutely invaluable practical help. Walter and Heather Williams are our nearest neighbours, and we couldn't wish for better. Heather has just retired as a nurse, and Walter as a stonemason, although they were both working when we moved in. Walter used to come to Upper Bridge

Court morning and evening to stoke the fires for the previous occupant, old Miss Bird. He wasn't overjoyed when we asked him if he could come and do some repairs for us. He suddenly appeared on the lawn like Don Giovanni's Commendatore and stood silently with folded arms while I made our requests. He said little, but looked into the distance with pursed lips. Gradually he accepted us, and now his friendship is as solid as a rock. His delightful wife, Heather, comes frequently to the back door with gifts of vegetables from their immaculate garden.

This is a lovely country habit: people appear at the door with offerings they have made or grown.

"Everything all right? I heard you had a nasty cold."

During the week of our arrival at Upper Bridge Court we had many gifts of fruit and vegetables, including some from Joyce Baker who had helped Miss Bird in the house and garden. Joyce had found Miss Bird at peace in her armchair one morning, and after her death she had helped to empty the crowded old house of a lifetime's possessions, and left it clean and tidy for us. She also lit the ancient Aga before our arrival so that we would have something to cook on. We had no stores and no pots and pans that first night, but the following evening Roger cooked a spaghetti bolognese, on the water-heating section of the old Aga, the same meal he had cooked for me when we first met.

We were surrounded by people in London and yet everyone was isolated in their own busy world. Here I know that we will always find help and support. Perhaps we have had to earn it.

Soon after we arrived, Joyce gave us a copy of the Resources Catalogue. This is a small directory which was compiled in the 1980s and has since been updated several times. It contains a list of all the local inhabitants, their telephone numbers and addresses, their interests, and the services they can offer. It also lists general information about doctors, vets, blacksmiths, libraries, post offices, churches, and so on. It won an award for services to the community, and is invaluable to both newcomers and established residents alike. There is also a monthly newsletter which updates all local information, and in which you can advertise your services or produce. In our latest Penta Paper, covering five parishes, there was a news item about Richard and Rachel Morgan's new baby, and a review of the talk I had given to the W.I. about my life before I came to live here!

Once we decided to become farmers, we realised that we would have to change our car to a four-wheel drive vehicle. But we made a mistake; we bought the V8 petrol version of the Discovery, which gobbled fuel. Consequently, it was not long before we exchanged it for the smaller, but much more economical, Daihatsu Fourtrak.

We have been agreeably surprised to find that, far from having fewer facilities for home delivery, there are actually far more. When I was a young married woman, living in London, the local grocer, butcher, and wine merchant would deliver to your door – but not any more. Here we have all these deliveries, and additionally fish that comes overnight from Cornwall (fresher than we could buy in London from our local fishmonger), plumbing and building supplies, and a mobile library. We also have a mobile hairdresser, chiropodist, and of course a mobile farrier for the horse! He comes in a van, fully equipped with a small gas furnace and anvil, and the horseshoes are bespoke! We don't get newspapers or milk delivered, although the latter can be delivered to the bottom of the road. Of course, we have plenty of our own milk, and we now print selected articles every Sunday from over the Internet.

The other agreeable surprise was that there are more good restaurants within a half-hour drive than we had in London. They may be further as the crow flies, but we can reach them in fifteen to thirty minutes. We have retained our London habit of eating out once a week, because it gives us a reason for getting out of our farm clothes and making ourselves look presentable – and we also enjoy good food and wine!

Trips further afield take a bit of organising. We have to get a farm sitter in, and someone both available and capable of looking after our mixed bunch of farm animals is not easy to find. We have two good farm sitters, but they have to be booked well in advance – not in the lambing season nor during public holidays. Consequently, excursions to see family or friends take a lot of management, and I do miss the freedom of being able to do things when we feel like it. Friends and family come to see us of course, and my sister Gil and her husband Mick took a holiday nearby so we could see a bit more of each other. After nearly three years here, we have managed one holiday ourselves, in Venice, which was like another world, and we loved every minute of it, especially the long evenings overlooking the water and eating wonderful food that someone else had cooked!

Back on home ground, the Morgans took us to the Kington Progressive Supper. This was a social occasion, and proceeds were given to the Kington Horse Show. The guests were split into groups, and each group took each course in a different house, until several hundred people finally met in a converted barn for dessert (the choice was staggering), and entertainment went on until the small hours.

We met more of the village community in church. People introduce themselves, ask what we are doing, and often have interesting suggestions to make. There is a rota whereby members of the congregation read the lesson and help in the church. At Christmas time the midnight Mass is held by candlelight, and hundreds of candles are the only light in the church. At our first Christmas service, a tray of small candles set fire to the wooden table on which they were resting, and had to be carried out and flung into the snow with all haste!

The only play we went to, in our first year away from the West End, was *The Curse of the Italian Postman*, performed by the village Youth Club. The audience sat on straw bales in a barn belonging to one of the villagers. Although we all enjoyed ourselves hugely, the young performers were clearly having the time of their lives!

Even for local excursions such as these, we have to organise our animals. When we arrived at Upper Bridge Court we had two dogs and two cats. Xanadu is a Groenendael Belgian Shepherd bitch, whom we had taken on at the age of four after her owner died, and after the death of our German Shepherd. Xanadu was a show dog, but had been to several homes, and was a nervous wreck and terrified of other dogs. We noticed, however, that she was not frightened of small white dogs, so we decided that a small white companion would be a good idea. I had had big dogs for many years, so we thought that a white German shepherd puppy would fit the bill and perhaps Xanadu wouldn't realise that he was getting bigger! We eventually found a breeder who lived on a strange Animal Farm in Surrey, with parrots, monkeys, horses, and ferocious white German Shepherds on chains. Well, the puppy we chose looked healthy, plump and cuddly, and was registered with the Kennel Club, so we purchased this tubby bundle of white fluff. We decided to call him Płatek Śniegu which is Polish for Snowflake.

Płatek now weighs 50 kilos and needs firm discipline, but Xanadu loves him and hasn't seemed to notice that he has grown twice as big as her. Płatek and Xanadu went off for six weeks over the moving period to a dog handler called Brian Gough, who guaranteed to cure any dog from chasing livestock – and so it has proved.

Our two cats, Zala and Tzarina, were therefore the first of our animals to take up residence. They were both Russian Blues, the last of a series of cats we had had over the years, and definitely to be described as townies. Zala was then twelve years old, a little stick of a cat, full of character, a shoulder cat, extremely affectionate, yet very independent and completely fearless. He had come with us to New York, where we lived for two years, with his sister Zara, who, sadly, was run over – a terrible day. When Zala was about six months old, my son Michael came over for a visit with two of his St Paul's school mates. They had all decided to stay longer in America, and had found a small apartment in downtown Manhattan. One of the boys, Sam, was going to stay in the apartment overnight before going on to Boston to take up a job. They hired a car for the removal, packed up their belongings, and we said goodbye to them all. That evening, we couldn't find Zala. We had been frantically searching the neighbourhood, getting increasingly worried as darkness fell. Zala would always come racing home when we called him, so if he didn't appear, something was wrong. Then the telephone rang: fortunately Sam had opened his suitcase soon after they arrived at the apartment and out staggered a very bewildered and disorientated little cat. Well, they drove all the way back to our house in Larchmont with Zala, and he appeared none the worse for his adventure (but he certainly wouldn't have survived a trip to Boston in the baggage hold).

Tzarina is plump and timid and rarely strays more than a few yards from the house, but Zala was as fearless as ever and roamed far and wide. We had confined both the cats to the house for two weeks after the move from London, but, a few weeks after that, Zala didn't come in when we called him. We searched for him for days; after two weeks, the nights were getting cold, our hopes had faded, and our hearts were heavy. We were asleep one morning when the telephone rang at about 7 a.m. Roger answered the phone and left the room without speaking. He went to the front gate in his dressing gown. When he came back tears were streaming down his cheeks, and he was holding the gaunt body of our Zala in his arms.

He was alive! He had been found by a farmer's wife several fields away, who had read his tag, and brought him home to us. Somehow our little townie had kept himself alive – just. Such a gift.

The Aga that Walter used to stoke morning and evening was our sole means of hot water and cooking. It was over fifty years old and fuelled by coal, which it gobbled up to the tune of £200 a month. The coal was kept in the old pigsty and had to be carried around the house, two hods, morning and evening. The ashes had to be riddled and carried outside. This procedure caused the Aga to belch clouds of coal dust which seeped into every nook and cranny. On the third day it belched more than usual: a thick fog filled the kitchen and a landslide of black soot covered the top of the Aga. This was the first of several.

Everyone said, "Oh, you must have an Aga in the country!" So we persevered. The larger half of the Aga had not been used. This was actually the cooker. We cleaned out the mice nests and the rust, and had the chimney swept. After several attempts we managed to get the fire going. The cooker had a separate mouth for coal, and a separate exit for riddling. Our efforts redoubled, the coal dust redoubled, Roger's trips to the pigsty redoubled. It was the spur to starting the central heating. Roger has installed central heating before. "It will take eight weeks," he said confidently. It took nearly a year.

The day the oil tank was delivered, we asked our neighbours to help us get it into the shed. We had been given several suggestions as to how to get the heavy tank from the driveway and into the shed, one of which was to roll it on logs, but it would still have had to be lifted onto its foundations. Roger put on his thinking cap, and built a rope cradle around the tank, with poles rather like a sedan chair, with which the team easily carried it to its resting place at the first attempt. I think he was a lot more pleased than he let on that a townie had solved the problem!

One of our town habits we have definitely retained is drinking champagne on the smallest possible excuse. One autumn day we were doing just that, sitting in the sun in front of the house on an old pig bench which we had found in the cellar. In front of us stretched the rolling fields of the north vista, dotted with sheep and cattle, their faint calls floating towards us. We were tired and content, sipping champagne in the sunshine. We looked at our grassed courtyard, which was taking a lot of cutting. "Geese are supposed to do a good job of keeping the grass down," I said.

We bought a book about geese and decided that Brecon Buffs were very handsome, and, being of local origin and a hardy breed, these were the ones we selected. We found an advertisement for a pair of Brecon Buff geese in the local paper, and went off to

Crickhowell, over the Welsh border, to see them. The Taylors had hens, geese, and some little pink piglets which were racing around in a small field. The pigs appeared to be having some sort of game with a piece of wood which they passed to each other at high speed. I was intrigued.

The geese were all driven down from the field for us to look at. The Brecon Buff goose and gander were cream with buff markings and pink beaks and feet. They looked a fine pair and we arranged to collect them in a few days – but it took more than a few days to prepare the shed for the geese. It had once been a calf shed and was long and low with thick stone walls and a stone-tiled roof. When I had cleaned out the rubbish, we found that the walls and door were very dilapidated, and Roger had to abandon his other jobs and set to work repairing the shed. When he started to remove the rotten facing boards, it became obvious that the whole front would have to be rebuilt, including inserting a supporting oak pillar and remaking the door.

Roger did a fine job. When he finished, we realised that we would have to buy some straw. We again looked in the local paper, and tracked down some straw for sale. David Griffiths lent us his stock trailer, we collected the straw bales, and laid a thick bed of straw in the shed. The surplus bales we stacked around the inside walls.

Off we went that evening to collect the geese in the borrowed trailer. When we got home, we backed the trailer right up to the goose shed door, opened the back of the trailer and made enticing noises. Very slowly the young pair emerged from the back of the trailer, looked around, and waddled majestically down the ramp into their new house. We felt triumphant. We decided to call them Boris and Barbara after Boris Becker and his wife (we're keen tennis fans!). Boris and Babs the Brecon Buffs.

The next morning we couldn't wait to see our new arrivals. I opened the door and went in cautiously. Only one goose! I searched frantically – "Rog! Come quickly! Someone's stolen our goose!"

Feverishly we searched again.

Roger gave a cry of triumph, "Here she is!"

A pair of pink feet and a pointed behind were projecting from between two straw bales: Babs had got herself wedged head first and was firmly stuck. We extricated her gently and set her on her feet. Boris made a great fuss of her, and with much flapping of wings they walked majestically out of the shed door into the grass courtyard. I hoped she hadn't been stuck all night, but she seemed none the worse for her ordeal.

The geese became very tame, and liked to stay by my side when I was working in the garden. They would take my gloves when I wasn't looking and put them on the ground, like cushions, to sit on. They were always together and would twine their necks affectionately. Boris would stroke Babs' back with his beak.

It was in the spring, when the neighbours were helping us to install the oil tank, that we first saw them mating vigorously in the mud. We had had several estimates for building a pond, but they had been too expensive to implement, so the geese had buckets to dunk their heads in. However, the lack of a pond didn't inhibit their mating activities, and soon Babs began to look for somewhere to lay. Roger had made a coop, so that the eggs and the goslings would be safe from rats, and we put the coop into the goose shed. But Babs kept making nests in the courtyard, and started laying under a bush. Our books didn't tell us what to do about this, so we telephoned The Domestic Fowl Trust. They were very helpful, and told us to fence off the bush, take the coop as near to it as possible, and put the eggs inside the coop. When we let Babs out of her shed the next morning, she tried furiously to get through the netting into the bush, but, by offering her grain, we enticed her over to the coop, and when she saw her eggs she sat on them, and promptly laid another one! Over the next few days, we moved the coop a few yards each day, until it was near the goose shed. Babs continued to lay an egg on alternate days, with Boris making his contribution in-between. On the advice of The Domestic Fowl Trust, we removed all the eggs each day except the two most recent ones. Babs would only leave the coop once or twice a day, to stretch her legs, eat, and drink. Boris manned a twenty-four hour guard beside her door, and became fiercely protective. When she had laid about twenty-five eggs, she began to sit, and we put back the twelve most recently laid eggs.

Boris was now a different bird: he would rush at anyone or anything that dared to come near his dear wife in her present condition. Neck outstretched and hissing fiercely he would race towards any intruder.

The first casualties were the builders arriving for work: when Boris came bombing towards them they legged it back to the gate and clambered over, helter-skelter! Casualty number two was Płatek. Płatek and Boris had always indulged in playful warfare, advancing and retreating towards each other with a great deal of noisy enjoyment. But now Boris advanced in earnest and made a violent peck at Płatek's flank, waddling off triumphantly with a beakful of white fur. Płatek was dumb-struck for a moment, then he seized Boris by the neck, lifted him off the ground, and shook him vigorously, before dropping him non too gently on the ground. Boris lay still. Our hearts stood still. Then slowly he got to his feet, and, with great dignity, waddled away with his head held on one side at a most awkward angle. He waddled over to Babs and told her in a rather cracked voice that he had successfully defended her from marauders. His neck soon recovered, but he was undeterred, and Płatek was soon attacked again; and again retaliated in the same way. They seemed to know how far they could go with each other – certainly Boris could have hurt Płatek quite badly, but then Płatek could quite easily have bitten his head off!

I myself got a peck on the hand when I was shutting them away for the night, but I used Płatek's method of getting the upper hand – I seized Boris firmly by the neck, held his head a few inches away from my face, and said very severely, "Just what do you think you're doing?"

Boris shook his head, lowered it meekly, and walked nonchalantly away, as if to say, "Just testing, just testing."

We were anxious that the anticipated goslings might come to some harm, as we had seen some evidence of rats in both the barn and the goose shed, so we summoned Leo the rat man. Rats are a farmer's enemy, and there is nothing for it but to get rid of them. Our two little house cats were not very effective ratters – or mousers either – and trying a rat cage-trap only caught a bird (which we released). Leo put down some poison in tubes, and we got rid of the rats for the time being. Although we still had to put down poison occasionally, we didn't like the process, and decided we would have to acquire some barn cats.

A pair of rats can produce 800 progeny in a year. Our neighbours can remember when rats were a major problem. The rats would move from farm to farm in droves, making the road impassable. If you met them when you were on a bicycle, you would have to coast along with your feet on the handlebars, or get severely bitten. Rats will eat their own kind when hungry, and you may find a half-eaten rat in a trap. The rats would make nests in the hay ricks, and when the time came to start using the ricks, the farmers used to fence them off so that, as the ricks were demolished and the rats emerged, they could club them to death. Survival can be savage.

Babs hatched her eggs at the end of April and had six healthy goslings, but I found one still struggling to get out of the broken shell, very cold and wet. Babs was fussing around the others, but didn't want to know about this little chap, who was very weak and couldn't even hold his head up. I popped him inside my jacket to keep him warm while I cleaned away the broken shells and wet straw. Margaret Morgan came to the gate with Lee, the first time we had met them, and I showed her the little gosling. She said I was doing the right thing by keeping 'the gull' warm in my jacket, but he would need hand-feeding with chick-crumb pellets, and she volunteered to take him home and look after him. After about ten days she returned him to us, strong and chirpy, still very small. He'd been living in a cardboard box in front of their Aga, and Margaret had fed him, initially by force, every few hours. Babs accepted him immediately, and he soon caught up with his brothers and sisters. Never was there such a proud father as Boris. How he fussed over his brood, how he crooned over Babs. At night he would squash into the coop with his family and tuck some of the little chicks under his wings. We had tried to put a stop to this invasion, initially, because we'd been told that the gander might attack the goslings, but he set up such a clamour that we gave in, and all concerned seemed delighted with the arrangement.

When the chicks were about a week old, we attached a long run to the coop so that they could peck the grass. They soon outgrew this, and we released them into the courtyard, hovering around them anxiously. Boris and Babs stretched their necks and hissed at us. Płatek was very interested in the new arrivals, but he got the same reception. Wounded, he went and sat by himself to watch the activities. The goslings seemed to think he was a large white goose and came cheeping around him. Płatek sat still while they investigated. Boris and Babs honked apprehensively, but waited in the wings.

One small chick settled down between Płatek's legs for a snooze!

When the goslings had lost their down and begun to sprout feathers, we made a small pond out of an old stone sink. From the pleasure this gave all the geese, we decided that we must do something about building a larger one, and they now have a small puddled-clay pond in the courtyard.

The goslings grew fast. Soon the flock had made a good job of mowing the courtyard grass, and we decided to give them the freedom of the paddock during the day. Each morning we would herd them through the courtyard and into the paddock, Płatek rounding up the stragglers. When they reached the centre of the green expanse, the whole flock would run across the grass on their toes, wings stretched out, like a troupe of ballerinas. Whenever we heard the rush of wind made by this dance, we would stop what we were doing to watch their flight. It never failed to lift our hearts.

By September it was hard to tell the goslings from their parents. They had grown into fine young geese, and the time had come for a parting of the ways. We were lucky indeed that we sold five of them for breeding. Sexing them was extremely difficult, and we sometimes got it wrong! I was sad to see them go. Two were left, and we decided to have one for Christmas dinner, and send the other to Roger's sister Janet and her husband Tony for their Christmas present. So we had to slaughter them. As usual, we'd read up as much as possible on the subject, and had obtained a copy of a very good booklet published by the Humane Slaughter Association called *Practical Slaughter of Poultry*. I told Roger I couldn't do it, and the task fell to him, but, having killed nothing in his life other than insects, as Christmas approached, he became increasingly concerned about the impending task.

Roger had just finished building a small guest bathroom, and we'd employed a local craftsman, Ikey Johnson, to plaster it for us. It turned out that Ikey had kept geese, and had killed more than he could remember. He offered to come up a couple of Sundays before Christmas and show us how to kill the first one. Ikey arrived, and took a heavy, straight branch of wood out of his car, about three or four feet long and two or three inches thick. Roger caught the goose and they went into the quiet and privacy of the barn. Ikey held it by its legs and wing tips, and lowered it so that its head was resting on the ground. Roger placed the branch across the back of its neck as close as possible to its head, Ikey placed his feet on each end of the branch and pulled upwards on the goose's legs. The vertebrae separated immediately, breaking the spinal cord and killing the goose instantly.

Margaret Morgan had offered to show us how to pluck and dress the goose, and Roger took it over to their farm as soon as Ikey had gone. Margaret and Lee were ready for him, dressed in cotton smocks, and had set up a table and chairs in one of the sheds off the yard, with a large box for the feathers, and electricity for a clothes iron. A clothes iron? Lee explained that the large feathers in the wings and tail should be plucked first, as they were the toughest and they would be easier to pluck whilst the goose was still warm. These large feathers are very hard to pull out, and Roger had to resort to doing them one at a time. After finishing the wings, they did the legs, and then started on the breast, but these smaller feathers had become quite difficult to pull out, because the goose had now cooled down. Margaret switched on the clothes iron and ironed the goose's breast! There was a pronounced difference, and the feathers came out much more easily than before. Lee and Roger continued plucking until all the feathers had been removed, and then carried the goose to the scullery, where they turned it over the flame from a shallow dish of methylated spirits, to burn off the remaining wisps.

Finally, they removed to the kitchen table, where Margaret proceeded to dress the goose. Neatly, she cut a hole between the vent and the parson's nose and inserted a couple of fingers, working them around inside the bird to separate the innards from the carcass. When they were loose, she cut right round the vent and pulled the innards out. She removed the head, feet, and wing tips, and arranged the goose so that its neck was tucked under one wing, the liver held in the fold of the other, and a sprig of parsley was placed on top. She'd also thought of freezing a tall, slim bottle of water which she pushed inside the goose, and surrounded it with flexible ice-cube packs to help preserve it on its journey to Janet and Tony.

Lee and Margaret had spent all morning showing Roger these skills, and since then he's put them to good use, but he now skins hens instead of plucking them, as skinning is a good deal quicker than plucking. He can skin and dress a hen in three-quarters of an hour, and this time will become a little shorter with practice.

Killing the goose for Janet and Tony had been very quick and simple. Ikey had used one of the methods we had read about, probably the only one that doesn't need any equipment, other than the branch of wood. But Roger still had to kill the goose we were going to eat for Christmas dinner.

My daughter Lesley and her family were staying with us, and Roger had planned to kill the goose on Christmas Eve. Lesley's partner, Maciek, agreed to help, but unfortunately he overslept. Roger paced up and down in the courtyard nervously, wanting to get it over with but frightened to do the deed by himself. At twelve o'clock he decided he must get it over with and strode over to the goose shed. Watching anxiously from the window, I saw him walking across the courtyard to the barn, holding the goose gently, stroking her neck and talking to her all the way. He went into the barn and closed the door behind him. He afterwards described how he had lowered her to the ground, holding her firmly by the legs, and how she had placed her head on the ground obligingly. He then placed an iron bar across the back of her neck, put his feet on the bar either side of her head, and pulled her legs upwards as strongly as he could. He felt the vertebrae separate immediately, accompanied by a violent flapping of the wings. The flapping wings made him think that he hadn't succeeded in killing the bird, and he was filled with dread. He knelt down to check that the vertebrae had severed, and felt a gap of about two inches between the base of the head and the neck bones. The bird had died instantly.

Now it had to be plucked and dressed. Maciek arrived, very contrite that he was too late to lend moral support for the slaughter, but he and Roger then set to and plucked the bird, after which it was hung for a few days to mature. Finally Roger dressed and cooked our goose, and we all had it for Christmas dinner on the 29th, when the rest of the family arrived – it tasted pretty good!

The geese had done a good job of keeping the grass mown in the courtyard, but I was trying to restore order in the garden. When I was clearing out one of the sheds, I found an old wooden sign saying 'GARDEN OPEN TODAY'. Heather and Walter told me that the garden used to be open to the public, and teas were served. In those days there was also a tidy vegetable garden, but now there was nothing but weeds and ivy; a lot of rusty old fence netting; posts; and years of accumulated rubbish. There was also a rickety fence dividing the ground behind the house, and on one side of it a corrugated steel garage. The remaining area of garden had a few old rose beds, very unkempt, and a border beside the hedge which had been swamped with ground elder and Michaelmas daisies. I decided to sit down and draw a new garden plan. The vegetable garden went on hold, but we thought we would enlarge the allotted area by taking a small piece of ground off the paddock. When I had finished my design, poor Roger had to come and help me once again, because I wanted the fence and garage knocked down! This really opened up the ground behind the house, and we could now see across to the paddock and field edges. I decided to dig everything out of the beds, lay all the plants on the grass, mark out the new beds, and then replant, digging up the weeds and ground elder as I went. This turned out to be a massive operation. The plants had now died back, and I was uncertain what some of these huge clumps were! Some of the gnarled old shrubs had roots too big to be dug out, and we had to pull them out with the Discovery. When I eventually got them all replanted (in fits and starts), I had to turf over the old beds with bits of grass dug up from here, there and everywhere, stamping them in with an old post banger that we found in the cellar.

Well, it will never look like a landscaped garden, but it's very open, pleasant, and colourful, and I shall be moving things around and replanting for years – like every gardener.

There were two visitors to the garden who were not at all pleased with all this disruption: the pheasants. They were living in our little wood when we arrived, and had raised a family of chicks which they used to bring into the overgrown garden. After the chicks had grown and left the nest, the parents continued to visit us, and we would encourage them with grain. Now they come every day during the winter, and call impatiently if there is no grain for them!

Although we had been so thrilled at the green, green appearance of Upper Bridge Court, a lot of that effect was caused by the ivy, which grew over everything – over walls, buildings and trees. It was growing into the stone walls and causing them to break up, and towering for 6 feet above them. It grew up the sides of the house and outbuildings, up and into the stone roof tiles, causing them to split and to slip. We started on the house, chopping the stems at the base and pulling the top growth off with rakes. Then we attacked the courtyard wall. This turned out to be an even harder job: the trunks were up to a foot wide in places, and the branches grew right through the dry-stone walls. When we had chopped off the worst of it, Roger said he would continue the work for an hour every morning. After he had been doing this for a few weeks, he began to get pins and needles and pains in his hands and arms from constant use of crowbars and hammers, so we had to abandon it temporarily, and Roger turned his attention back to the house.

The plumbing at Upper Bridge Court had to be completely replaced. The water tanks were very old, and located in a room we wanted to use as a bedroom; the hot water was heated by the coal-fired Aga which we planned to remove; we wanted to install a full central heating system; and we wanted to move the existing bathroom and build two more.

Roger had installed central heating in several of the houses he had lived in over the years. He enjoyed doing it, and it had worked well. Going on past experience, he told me the plumbing would take him two months – but it was ten months before the central heating was switched on, partly because we had started to set up the farm, and partly because he had underestimated the size of the job. Roger plans everything very meticulously (I rush at things). He took well over a month planning the installation carefully, so that all the radiators were of the right size and in the correct positions: eighteen radiators; a large boiler; an oil tank; two hot water tanks; new storage tanks; and a lot of piping. The ceiling below the loft space had to be rebuilt to squeeze the new cold water storage tanks above them, and several holes had to be knocked through the exterior stone walls, which are two feet thick at ground level. Not one pipe will be visible when the whole house has been decorated – and that took a lot of planning, with our stone walls and stone-tiled floors.

Roger was still working on the central heating, but we had reached the stage when there was some major building work to be done, and it was time to call in the cavalry. Could we have a porch made while the builders were invading? The garden was in reasonable shape, and we would have liked somewhere sheltered to sit and look at it occasionally. In London we had a porch at the back of the house, and spent many a refreshing hour sitting there having a drink and a chat, looking at the garden, or even working – I did most of my writing on the porch.

It would be a luxury which we could ill afford, and which we had discussed when we first saw the house. It also meant applying for listed building consent. The answer was yes, and we have never regretted it. Sometimes it's worth a few sacrifices to fulfil a dream. Because Upper Bridge Court is a listed building, we have to obtain consent for any changes we'd like to make. We're very keen to keep the house and the outbuildings as they were when they were built at the beginning of the eighteenth century and, therefore, the appropriate department in our local council has been sympathetic to the requests we've made so far.

We used David Taylor, an architect in Leominster, to design the changes we wanted and to obtain approval for them from the council. A lot of the work needed ironwork for the doors and windows, and David put us in touch with a blacksmith, Peter Crownshaw of St Michael's. Peter is one of those rare people who has an artistic flair and an engineering skill with which to express it. He's made many hinge straps, pintles and bolts, for the house, barn and pigsties. His *pièce de résistance* was the knocker for the front door, and the Suffolk latches for the front and back doors. We told him what we wanted and left the design to him. The two latches are very different in style, but both are simple and graceful. The knocker is a large iron ring, held on the double-thickness oak front door with what looks like a very large split pin. It complements the front of the house perfectly.

We had already had a massive amount of replastering done, and a damp course put in, but the floors were in a bad way. They were tiled, but a rather brazen red, laid directly on to the earth over a thin layer of concrete. We thought that it would be wonderful to go back to a flagstone floor, as it had been originally. It transpired that this would necessitate digging up the whole of the ground floor to a depth of 8 inches, and all the furniture would have to be taken out of the rooms, with the exception of the sitting room, which had a suspended wooden floor over the cellar. We also wanted to open up the stone steps to the cellar, which had been blocked off, and to repair the dormer windows, which leaked badly. Whilst the rooms were in chaos, we could have the red brick fireplaces taken out, and see what was behind them.

We had been searching since our arrival for some more stone tiles to repair the roofs and dormers, but they are difficult to get hold of. The tiles vary in size from several feet to 6 inches across; the larger ones are positioned at the eaves, and the size diminishes towards the apex. They are about an inch thick, and all cut by hand from stone – not a process that can be done in a factory. A process of making similar tiles from stone chippings has now been invented, and these are easy to obtain and not so expensive. However, you cannot mix them successfully with the old hand-cut tiles. By this time I was looking every week at the advertisements in the local paper, because we needed so many things which sooner or later turned up in its columns. Sure enough, we saw some stone tiles advertised. We went immediately to look at them, but there were several prospective buyers, and the owner of the barn which was being demolished decided to take bids in sealed envelopes. We weren't successful.

Some time later we heard by word of mouth of another lot of tiles in the possession of a local demolition contractor. This time we were first on the scene, and bought a good quantity of excellent tiles. With the help of our builder, we got them all back to Upper Bridge Court, where we sorted them into sizes, and stored them in the barn.

Whilst the floors were being done the house was going to be impossible to live in, so we decided to move into the local inn for the week. The dogs would have to go back to Brian Gough for a refresher course, and the cats would have to go to a cattery. The inn is only a couple of minutes away so we could come up every day to care for the livestock.

Even with our sanctuary at the inn, it was difficult to bear the invasion, and we decided to regard this as a holiday and indulge ourselves in one of our favourite pastimes: every lunch time we took two chairs into the paddock, and ensconced ourselves under the oak tree with a bottle of champagne. We were accompanied by the geese, whom we put in the paddock every morning to escape the chaos in the courtyard. The geese enjoyed our company, and were very attentive, but it wasn't until too late that we realised they were also pecking the chair cushions from behind, making holes which looked as if an army of mice had been at work, and through which the sponge stuffing burst out!

We found just what we had hoped for behind the red brick fireplaces – open fireplaces – but when the work began on the floors, one of the walls began to collapse. The wooden supports had rotted at the base, and when they were disturbed, they gave way. Although a prop was immediately put into position, the floor above had dropped, and now our bedroom floor is lower on one side than it was previously!

As everybody knows who has had builders in, the noise and the dirt are unbearable, and although they were doing a splendid job, we couldn't wait to get them out of the house, and have a bit of peace and privacy again. They were there all through the long hot summer of 1994 and it was two years before we could face any more major work.

During the first winter we had to rely on a motley collection of different heating systems, including wood burners, storage heaters, tiny radiators (running off the Aga) and electric fires. The small kitchen was always at 90 degrees because of the Aga, but most of the rooms were rather cold. We were therefore both delighted to switch on the central heating just before our second winter. It all works very well, and we're as warm as toast, even when the north wind blows hard against the front of the house in midwinter.

We hadn't been warned about the electricity cuts and the water cuts, but we've learned to read the warning signs and start lighting candles. David Griffiths introduced us to Big Jenny – not his girl friend, but his portable generator – and we've now bought one of our own to keep the central heating, freezers and television going in emergencies. We've even begun to think about buying a new Aga, oil-, not coal-fired!

The water is a problem that we've not yet solved. Because we're at the top of a hill we're the first to have no water when the pressure goes and the last to get it back. It can be off for several days. Welsh Water deliver us a bowser containing 200 gallons of water, and we have to ferry it into the house. But the worst problem is watering the stock, Roger having to carry 40 gallons a day from the house to the animals in the fields.

By January 1997 we had thirty piglets, two 10-month-old gilts, three sows and a boar, a cow and a bullock, fourteen ewes and a ram, a horse, two geese and a gander, twenty-six hens and three cocks, and they all had to have a constant supply of clean drinking water, when everything was completely frozen and the main water supply was cut off.

One frosty morning as I opened the bedroom curtains, I saw Roger letting the geese out of their shed. They always run out of the shed and across the courtyard, stretching their wings and honking. After they have stretched their legs, they waddle to the pond for a morning dip. But that was the first of the winter mornings when the pond froze over, and Swan Lake turned into Walt Disney's Fantasia on Ice! They looked strangely graceful in their efforts to get to the edge, first one leg and then the other shooting out from under them. The sunrise tinted the white ground pink, as if the performance was being rehearsed and lit for my benefit.

The Expansion

Animals are such agreeable friends – they
ask no questions, they pass no criticisms.

George Eliot

I don't think we realised what we were in for when we decided to get a pig. Roger said it would help us to plough the land, but I thought we were letting ourselves in for too much work. I weakened when we started to clear the land behind the barn. Thistles, brambles, shrubs and nettles grew chest high. A pig or two suddenly seemed a good idea, and I remembered the nice little pigs we had seen playing with a stick at the Taylors'. We wanted to continue to support rare breeds whenever possible, especially if they were native to the area, and Gloucester Old Spots or Tamworths went on the short list. I mentioned it in church one morning, and one of the congregation told us that there was a Gloucester Old Spot pig farm a few miles away. We went to see them, and immediately fell in love with these huge gentle animals with their floppy ears and Dalmatian spots. One of the older sows had farrowed the night before, and was lying in a straw-filled shed with her piglets. She was a massive animal, and her piglets were so tiny and beautiful. I was awestruck by the confidence of the pig farmer, Andrew Watson, who, with a slap and a push, moved the big animal aside to give us a better view of the piglets. We went to see the weaners (piglets about eight to twelve weeks old who had been weaned from their mothers), who lived in groups in large polytunnels. They were captivating. They raced around, full of beans, rushing to eat and drink from their troughs, then galloping away to play. Having seen how huge these animals became, I was somewhat daunted at the thought of managing them, so we thought that we would buy a couple of weaners, in order to get used to them gradually.

When we got home, common sense took over and I thought it would be prudent just to look at some Tamworths, as they are known to be excellent rooters (they are also in the highest category of breeds threatened with extinction). This time it was Roger who dragged his feet; he wanted to get on with re-plumbing the house and spend no more time searching. I telephoned the secretary of the Tamworth Society, Barbara Warren, to see if there were any Tammies in our area and she told us that one of her boars was currently visiting a lady who had two Tamworth sows. Roger reluctantly accompanied me to see Diana Palmer. She had a smallholding with a Jersey cow, some sheep, and two sows. She took us out to the patch of land where the pigs were living. Two corrugated pig arks squatted in the mud. Then suddenly, in each doorway, loomed a huge orange form, and two giant teddies trundled out, closely pursued by their massive suitor. I'm afraid we fell hook, line, and sinker, and the search was on for two Tamworth piglets.

We tracked down two female piglets, known as gilts, who had also been fathered by this boar of Barbara Warren's, and their breeder agreed to make a field ark for them (a shelter made of semicircular sheets of corrugated steel). We had to fence off the piece of land behind the barn, which we hoped they would plough up for us, and so this was our first contact with electric fencing. We've had plenty of dire warnings about getting caught up in the wire, and up to this point have managed to avoid it, although Roger once bent over too far and touched the wire with his head. His hat flew off pretty smartly – so Brian Morgan told me with much laughter!

The piglets arrived in an open trailer; small, orange and hairy, with pricked ears and pointed noses. We were immediately besotted and have remained so ever since. We made a great fuss of them and gave them lots of attention. We christened them Tallulah and Tess. Tallaluh and Tess the Tamworths. They became very tame and extremely friendly.

Pigs are very clean and intelligent animals, supposedly the most intelligent quadruped other than the elephant. They were once trained very successfully to retrieve game when royal edict had proclaimed that no dogs were to be used for hunting unless they were small enough to jump through a horse's stirrup. They never soil their houses or bedding unless you give them no alternative. They love human contact, being talked to, being stroked. They will rush to you when they are called, and sink to their knees with pleasure when you stroke them, eventually collapsing on to their sides in ecstasy, exposing their vulnerable bellies for more, and squeaking mournfully when you tear yourself away.

One sunny morning, we took Tallulah and Tess into the paddock for a run. They got very excited by the green expanse and began to race about. Tess then started to gallop towards Roger, but Płatek thought this was an attack. Ignoring our calls, he launched himself at Tess and bit her hard on the back. He made quite a deep wound, and we thought it would be wise to show it to the vet, who said that Tess should have an injection of antibiotics. As the pigs were out of doors, he decided it would be easier to inject her in the ark, and asked us to block the doorway behind him when we had got the injured pig inside. "If I call to be let out, open the door quickly," he said.

"What if we don't hear anything?" quipped Roger.

I don't think the vet found this amusing, but in he crawled with his syringe in his pocket.

The ark rocked around violently, and then out he came – the deed had been done!

I had to inject the pigs myself at a later date, but I didn't fancy going into the ark with two large pigs and a syringe, even if they were friendly, so we planned to corner them in the paddock, where Roger would trap them with a hurdle. We cornered them without any trouble, but as soon as they saw the hurdle, they broke out to the side at high speed. We tried again. This time I stood astride Tallulah, stroking her the while – so far so good. I rammed the syringe into her rump, and she took off backwards, leaving me with my legs akimbo and the syringe still in my hand! I've now perfected the injection technique by waiting until feeding time, and, when they are gorging themselves, I stick the needle in. There is a slight reaction, but they continue to eat, then I attach the syringe and quickly discharge its contents!

Tallulah and Tess did a good job of digging up their patch of land, and we decided to move them to plough the overgrown vegetable garden. The pig ark was hitched to the Discovery and towed across the field. Luly and Tess were most indignant, and trotted behind the ark squealing loudly. But they soon settled in their new home.

They grew up fast, and it was time to think of breeding from them. Tallulah was more affectionate and gentle, and Tess was the boss. When they were eleven months old we arranged to have a boar in to serve them.

As with any animal, care must be taken, when looking for a mate, that the male is unrelated and, if possible, comes from a different lineage altogether. This is a more difficult task with rare breeds, as there are not many registered males to choose from, and they may be some distance away. The field was narrowed even further, because a gilt should be served by a young boar, as damage can be done to the young female frame by a large boar.

Some boars 'go out on the road', that is to say, they

will come to the sow's place of residence, but other boar owners insist that the sows come to them. In both instances this involves application for movement permits, and the animal must not be moved on for a further twenty days. We didn't want Tallulah and Tess to go away for three weeks, especially when we had seen some of the areas in which the pigs would be confined.

We eventually found a suitable boar who could come to us on the required date. He was Limes Glen TW/1/UCA/2/93, affectionately known as Billy. Billy came from Witney, near Oxford, and we arranged to go and collect him, and at the same time to have lunch with my Godmother, who lived in Oxford. She gave us a warm welcome, and showed no resentment that she had been fitted in to our boar collecting schedule, with the greater share of the timetable devoted to the boar! We decided against having lunch with Billy parked in the trailer outside, but to have lunch on the outward journey. This necessitated a quick change into 'pig clothes' in the trailer.

Billy looked a fine chap, but he was a great deal larger than we had been expecting, and with large protruding tusks. His owner put the fear of God into us by pulling up his trouser leg and revealing a long deep scar. This had been made by Billy turning his head 'a bit sharpish'. Billy went into the trailer willingly enough – perhaps he knew what lay in store after a trip in a trailer! He emerged into the field at the other end at a canter. Our two little gilts took one look at this huge animal and legged it in the other direction as fast as they could. But Billy was a pig of experience, and he soon had his new lady friends eating out of his trotter!

We were decidedly nervous of Billy to begin with, and only went in to the pig area armed with pig boards (hand-held boards to direct the pigs), as we had been instructed by his owner. Billy proved to be no gentleman as far as our little girls were concerned, and made sure that he got his share of the food, rudely knocking Tess and Tallulah out of his way. He also turfed them out of the pig ark, so that he had more room to stretch out his large form comfortably.

The night of Billy's arrival, it began to snow heavily while we were having supper. All the pigs were fed, and supposedly tucked up for the night, but Roger and I thought we'd better go and check on the sleeping arrangements. It was now dark, and, bundled up in our scarves and coats, we went up by torchlight to the pig ark, which was situated on the edge of a small wood. Sure enough, Billy was ensconced snugly in the ark, but Tallulah and Tess were lying nose to tail under a bush. We decided that we'd better build the gilts a shelter; we got an old gate and lashed it horizontally to a couple of trees at each end, built some walls out of straw bales, put a layer of straw on the ground, and tied a sheet of plastic on top of the gate, as a roof. All this took a considerable time, and several trips back to the barn, and of course Billy decided he'd better investigate the activities. Initially we held a pig board against our legs with one hand, but this was increasing the number of trips we had to make; it was snowing hard; and we were getting cold. So we abandoned the pig boards, but kept a wary eye on Billy. He watched the proceedings with great interest, snuffling helpfully at the straw. When we had finished he wasted no time in flinging himself full length onto the straw, with a sigh of approval. Tallulah and Tess turned tail and trotted off to their old quarters.

Before long Billy and the gilts were good friends, and we felt as pleased as punch when they all began to sleep together in the new shelter, squashed side by side like a string of large sausages.

Billy responded well to a bit of attention and a spot of slap and tickle, and we soon treated him like an old friend, and were sad when the time came for him to go. But he had done his job: we were most gratified when we found him apparently asleep on Tallulah's back, with an unmistakable smile on his face. A boar will take about twenty minutes to inseminate a sow, injecting her with about half a pint of sperm, and finishing off the job with a plug of jelly to keep it where he put it!

A female pig's gestation period is three months three weeks and three days, so, providing you have correctly diagnosed their oestrus, you can be well prepared for the great event. We had cleared out the two old pigsties in the courtyard, which had been filled with coal. Roger had rebuilt the front and made new doors, and Walter had repaired the stonework and built a surrounding stone wall. We had seen how Rosie Watson had sectioned off a corner of the building with a sheep hurdle in order to form a creep, and hung an infra-red lamp above to entice the piglets in to keep warm and escape from the bulk of their mother. I had been doing as much reading as possible, and felt reasonably confident with my nursing training behind me, even though pigs hadn't been on the agenda. Nevertheless, it was with some trepidation that we waited for Tallulah and Tess to go into labour.

The two adjoining sties had doors into the same small cobbled yard. Luly and Tess seemed pleased with their new quarters and flung themselves down on the clean straw with considerable abandon – in the same sty! We re-orientated them several times, but they were used to being together. We hung over them like anxious parents, but we were actually in the house when there was a knock on the door. Walter had been doing some stone-work for us. "I think you have some piglets," he said.

Out we raced. Tess had begun farrowing; several piglets were scuttling about strongly in the straw, but Tess didn't seem to know what was going on, and grunted in panic when a piglet appeared and charged at it angrily. We dried them off and put them under the lamp, where they soon settled down to sleep.

Almost immediately the next piglet appeared, slipping out softly into the straw. We cleaned off the mucus, made sure it was breathing, and popped it under the lamp with its siblings. Tess had seven piglets, but wouldn't accept any of them. We were lucky that we had such a good relationship with our pigs, because both of them totally accepted us during the farrowing, and seemed quite happy for us to handle the piglets. Again and again I tried to bring a piglet to suckle, but each time she turned on it angrily. I had tried everything the books suggested, and we were getting worried that the piglets would not get the vital colostrum in time, since this first milk contains antibodies against infection. I phoned Barbara Warren, who luckily was in. Breeders are invariably helpful when you turn to them for advice, and Barbara said, "Give her a pint of beer, wait for her to settle, and try again." It worked. Soon they were all sucking contentedly. Relief and infinite pleasure.

Tallulah went into labour a few days later, and behaved like an old hand. She had eight healthy piglets, and when she finished we put them all onto the teats. They were so tiny and vigorous, sucking fiercely and hungrily in a tidy row. We were full of pride and joy.

Tallulah and Tess still visited each other's sties, sleeping together nose to tail when they wanted a break from their demanding broods, and showing no animosity towards each other's piglets. We kept the piglets divided by low barriers across each of the sty doors, so that the sows could come and go, but the litters would not get mixed up before they were identified. We knew that to keep or sell pigs for breeding they must be registered with the British Pig Association and the Rare Breeds Society, and this had to be done by tattooing their ears with the allocated identification before they were three weeks old.

We borrowed the fierce-looking tattooing forceps from our neighbours the Morgans, who use them on their calves, and bought the additional characters we needed from the agricultural chemists. The forceps have slots in the end, into which you slide the square numbers and letters. These are made up of a series of needles which are punched through the animal's ear, after smearing it with tattooing paste. I wrote out a plan, and we set everything up on a folding table in the forecourt of the sty (the table was the props table from my One-Woman Shakespeare Show!). Luly and Tess were shut into their sties with their piglets, Roger went inside, and I set up shop in the little courtyard. He opened up the top half of the door, captured a piglet and held it over the door for me to do the grisly deed. The noise was indescribable. Long before I squeezed the forceps through its tiny ear, the piglet was making an ear-splitting, high-pitched squeal and the other piglets took up the chorus. The sows got worried and were crashing around, grunting, but made no attempt to attack Roger, standing bravely inside the sty. This process has now been repeated many times, but we were never so traumatised as on that first attempt. I think it hurt us more than the piglets.

When the piglets had all been marked, we removed the barriers, and they all started visiting each other. They would race from one side of the sty to the other, dashing through the dividing door and tearing around in excited circles. When it was feeding time, a miraculous division would occur, and each piglet would find its familiar teat, sometimes with both sows and their piglets squashed into the same sty. We never tired of watching these delightful and engaging animals and fussing over their proud parents.

One morning Luly wouldn't eat her breakfast. This was serious. That evening she vomited a little and again wouldn't eat. We called the vet. She thought Tallulah had erysipelas, which is a highly contagious and notifiable swine disease, and gave her an injection of penicillin. Luly was clearly in pain, and although she allowed the piglets to suckle, she lay still most of the time. I spent as much time as I could with her that day, stroking her and talking to her. She seemed to like my company and would raise her head and give a little grunt when I had to leave. When I went to bed Roger stayed up and went to look at her every half an hour. He came to bed about 2 a.m. He had decided not to wake me but I woke anyway.

His voice cracked, "She's dead."

Part of the process of having animals is losing them through sickness or death and all the distress that this entails. But nothing has been so shocking as the death of Tallulah.

We needed to know if she had indeed had erysipelas, as there were various precautions we would have to take. I had never been convinced that this was the case, as there had been no fever and there was no skin reddening. We wanted to have an autopsy, and the body had to be taken away. Tallulah weighed about 100 kilos and we could not move her ourselves. We called the professional knacker.

She lay alone in her sty, looking as if she was peacefully asleep. I lay down beside my dear friend, face to face; I put my arm around her and said goodbye.

When the knacker arrived, he could not get his truck with the winch on the back into a straight line near the pigsty, and we had quite a job to haul out her huge carcass. Slowly she was wound out of the sty, out of the little cobbled courtyard and onto the back of the truck. I stroked her ear as she passed. Dear Tallulah, how undignified we made your departure, yet you never lost your dignity.

Tallulah did not have erysipelas. She had died of a twisted gut, unusual in pigs. There was nothing we could have done, except perhaps to have shortened her pain.

We had shut her piglets away from her when she was clearly very ill, and now we were really worried as to what would become of them. They were three weeks old and just beginning to eat solid food. Barbara Warren again gave me some good advice – to give them some milk pellets. Hay and Brecon Farmers immediately arranged a special delivery from their fodder suppliers, but the piglets did not seem to be taking enough sustenance. Then a wonderful thing happened: Tess decided to adopt the eight little orphans. She called them to her, grunting and offering her teats. Soon she was feeding all fifteen piglets and her extra teats gradually filled with milk. There was no fighting, but Tess's piglets would always feed first. We gave all of them the milk pellets in addition to their food, and of course Tess got extra rations and lots of titbits. We have kept a female from each litter, Tinkerbell and Tulip.

Now that all the piglets were eating and drinking well, we decided it was time for them to leave the shelter of the sties, and to go out with Tess to pasture and an outside ark. We had Roger's daughter, Andrea, and her partner, Mark, staying with us at the time. Tess trotted obediently into the trailer, but we were very glad to have two extra pairs of hands to catch the slippery piglets. They were eventually all safely transferred to their new habitat and careered around full of excitement, exploring the long grass.

Andy and Mark gave us invaluable help every time they came to visit. This time it was transferring fifteen small agile piglets from the sty to the trailer and then to the vegetable garden, from where they had several sallies through the electric fence before they learned that it was more comfortable to stay inside with Mum!

Catching piglets is not an easy exercise! At a later date, when we moved the piglets out to the field, two of them got away as we were unloading them. They were off like the wind. We hastily got the rest behind the electric fence with Tess, and then gave chase. We chased them round the field for about fifteen minutes, until finally we cornered them in the hedge. I dived in and grabbed one and Roger grabbed the other. The poor piglets were terrified, and we were absolutely exhausted.

A month after we had moved Tess and her large family out of doors, the two litters were indistinguishable. I don't know who was the proudest – Tess, or Roger and I. The patch of land which they were now grazing and rooting was the area we were planning to make into a vegetable garden. Walter told us it had once been a very tidy vegetable plot, but that was before Miss French fenced it in to make a badger pen.

Miss French was the previous owner of Upper Bridge Court, and had moved here some forty years ago after taking fishing holidays in the area for many years. Miss Bird originally lived here as her companion. Wynne Bird was a kindly soul, held in great affection by all who knew her, but Miss French was a force to be reckoned with. She wore long tweed skirts, big boots, a stovepipe hat, and an enveloping black cloak. She had the first diesel Land Rover in the area, and would drive it so slowly that it kept coking up. She would then get the garage to rescue her. The son of the owner, now one of the directors, told us that he would give the engine a good run over the hills and return it to Miss French, who thought he was a miracle worker!

She kept a pet badger, which became so fierce that it had to have a pen made – in the vegetable garden. Walter was summoned to bury yards of wire netting in the ground and build a strong wall around, to keep in the wretched badger. It died in the end, and we have inherited miles of netting to dig up and cut down in order to plant vegetables. We have been so grateful to have had help from Maciek, Mark and Andy in this backbreaking task. Walter, as usual, had made a very good job of it. His name was taken in vain a few times!

Miss French was fond of a tipple. She had a drinking companion called Tom Davies. Tom did major work to the house, and I suspect that he and Miss French were responsible for the bottles which were buried all around the garden and in the hedges. They used to go down to the inn for a drink in the evening, and on more than one occasion the Land Rover had to be hauled out of the ditch by their neighbours. Miss French also had some terriers, which had to be kept in the garden with yet more wire fencing, to stop them chasing sheep.

We were surrounded by sheep, and had begun to think about having some of our own. When we got the news that we had a buyer for our house in London, we were actually in Australia, visiting my daughter, Lesley, who was living in Adelaide at the time, and had just had a baby (my first grandchild!). I had been at school near Melbourne for two years, and this seemed the ideal opportunity to make contact with my school friend Jenny Rau, whom I had often thought of, but had never written to. I was given her address by my old school, Toorak College, and we arranged to fly up and visit her. I was very excited. I had been to eleven schools, and it is hard to lose your close friends. When we met (for the first time in over forty years), it was as if we had never been parted. Jenny hadn't changed, and we got on as well as we had long ago. How I wish she lived near me now. She had a few sheep, which roamed around grazing freely.

"They're my lawn mowers," said Jenny.

"Are they difficult to look after?"

"Oh no! They look after themselves."

I remembered this conversation one day when Roger and I were leaning over the gate, looking across the field to the Wye Valley. There is a different view from every aspect of our farm: rolling hills and fields to the north, the Brecon Beacons to the south-west, the Clee Hills to the north-east, the Malvern Hills just visible in the east, the Wye Valley and the Black Mountains to the south. The long grass in the field in front of us needed topping. We would have to ask the Morgans for their help. But how about some sheep of our own? Jenny had said that sheep weren't any trouble.

We decided to get Hebridean Hill sheep, as they are very hardy, can winter out on our high pasture, and they are on the Rare Breeds endangered list. Through the Hebridean Society, we tracked down some ewes with lambs for sale in Shropshire, and off we went with our trailer. This was our first encounter with the wild animals that were to be 'no trouble'. The shepherd had penned our three ewes, together with their lambs. They were black, the ewes with rather ragged fleeces, as they had started their summer moult, and the lambs with dense black wavy coats. It took three of us to catch each one and get it into the trailer. The sheep leaped in the air like mad things – not at all the way normal sheep behaved! These antics were not an aberration. It took months before Roger and I could handle them. We tried all sorts of methods to drive them, including holding a long piece of cloth stretched between us – the books say this will work. The sheep evaded us without difficulty, racing around the barrier, leaping and kicking in disdain.

One day we were trying to get the sheep into the barn, me in front with some tasty titbits in a bucket, and Roger behind, ready to shut the door. With some difficulty we got the sheep into the courtyard. I couldn't tempt them into the barn, but managed to lead them into the old pigsty. Roger moved forward quickly to shut the gate, but at that moment the sheep realised it was a trap. As he put his hand on the gate, a living wall of black sheep charged him. The first sheep, flying through the air, head-butted him in the chest, knocking him flat on his back. The rest of the sheep ran over him one by one, trampling over his prostrate form. I'm afraid I was laughing too much to come to his aid.

Eventually we enlisted the help of a shepherd called John Matthews. I had telephoned him to enquire about a shepherd's crook he had invented, which had a retaining latch to imprison the sheep's leg. John arrived with his crook, and I asked him if he could give us a bit of instruction in handling our wild mob. We learned a lot from him. He was very quiet and gentle. No running or waving of arms, just some soft noises, everything done very very slowly. It was some comfort to hear that the behaviour of our little Hebrideans was atypical of the average flock of large white sheep! He showed us how to set up a race (a fenced passage for sheep), so that we could drive the sheep down the side of the barn, and how best to catch one that you needed to single out. We felt a lot more confident after his visit.

I had always spent time each day trying to get the sheep to come to me for titbits, and although this was paying off, they were still very nervous. I was determined to make them tamer, and I bought a sheep's bell which I used to ring whenever I appeared in their field. They gradually grew to associate this sound with soft words and titbits, and eventually they would come to greet me, and sometimes follow me! They are very tame now, almost like 'normal' sheep: we can even take Płatek with us when we herd or handle them. We have fourteen ewes now, but the original three ewes were Bramble, Camilla, and Titania, and we have a particularly soft spot for them.

Titania and Bramble had ewe lambs, Tizzy and Buzz, who became part of our flock, but Camilla had a wether, as a castrated ram, or ram lamb, is known. Wethers are sometimes run with a ram to keep him company, but usually they are sold for meat. As we hadn't got our own ram, we had always known that Compost, as he had been christened by his previous owners, would have to go in the autumn, or he would not make good meat, and we would not be able to sell him. We were not looking forward to taking Compost to the abattoir. I always felt that his brown eyes looked at me reproachfully, and he was the most nervous of the lambs. The time for his departure approached and we could delay it no longer. We arranged to take him to the abattoir early one autumn morning. My heart was heavy, and I couldn't look as Compost was herded out of the trailer and into the holding pen. The butcher was sympathetic, and said he remembered his first lamb long ago. We waited in the car for the skin, which we had to take immediately to the tanner. I was swallowing hard, determined not to be sentimental, but feeling very miserable indeed. The animals are treated kindly at the abattoir, and lose consciousness immediately when an electric stun-gun is held to their forehead. I couldn't look at the skin when it was brought out in a bag. We drove off in silence to the tanners.

It will never be easy taking our animals to the abattoir, but that first time was the worst. We always think of Compost when we drive past, although many of our animals have now been taken for slaughter. It is a necessary part of the pattern of farming life.

One morning I was reading the local paper over breakfast, when I came across an advertisement for the sale of a Jersey cow for £150. Roger had been longing for a house cow, but I wasn't very keen.

"It'll mean very early mornings, and we'll be completely tied," I said.

"Ah, but we'll have our own milk and butter and she'll manure the land," replied Roger.

"You can't milk a cow."

"I'll have to learn."

"Well, I'm not having anything to do with her. Is that agreed?"

When I saw the advertisement it suddenly seemed that the time was right. The pigs were such a delight and no trouble, perhaps a cow would be a good idea after all, and a Jersey was a friendly docile animal – so the books said.

The little cow was in a cow shed on a very run down farm. She was called Minnie, small and skeletally thin, with huge dark eyes. We retired into a corner for a discussion, and decided she had better be seen by a vet. The farmer could see we were novices, and said there would be no time for that, as he had other buyers waiting to see the cow. "Jerseys are always skinny," he said.

Back we went into the cow shed. She had nice big teats and he showed Roger how easy it would be to milk her. While this demonstration was going on, Minnie had violent diarrhoea, jetting out on to the wall behind her. I was sure that this was not the normal dung that the farmer assured us it was. It was evident from the cow shed floor that this little cow was not well. We left, but would dearly have liked to take Minnie. We decided to call the local vet to discuss the symptoms. Perhaps we could restore her to health. The vet knew the farm and he knew the little cow; he said she had Johne's disease, an infection of the bowels from which there is no cure.

"Don't touch her," was his advice.

Poor Minnie.

Some time later there was another advertisement,

this time for the reduction of a Jersey herd. This was only the second mention of a Jersey cow that we had seen in nearly a year, so off we raced. We had by now acquired our own second-hand stock trailer, and we took it with us 'just in case'. The books advised an older cow for beginners – she would be easier to handle and easier to milk. However, we thought that a big cow would be rather daunting, and after all, we had soon learned to handle our little Tamworths.

This farm was tidy and run by a mother and daughter. They treated their dairy herd well and were on friendly terms with them all. They took us to see the young heifers who were in a small field by a stream. They were pretty and friendly, and we favoured a pale cream one called Emral Constellation. Unfortunately she seemed a bit flighty, but the women assured us that she was halter trained and also that she came from a very quiet family. They took us to see the heifer's aunt, who came over to us when she was called and was very gentle. The deal was made. She cost £475. They knew we wanted her and wouldn't bargain – we now know better than to look too clean and tidy when we go to make a purchase!

It took four of us to get Emral Constellation into the barn and from there into the trailer. Once she was safely battened down, we went into the house to get her papers. When we came back, she was trying to climb out of the back of the trailer, although the gap was a good deal higher than her head.

"She'll soon settle down when you start driving."

We could hear her trying to climb out every time we slowed down!

POT OF GOLD

"I knew this was the place"

Boris and Babs, the proud parents

One small chick settled down with Płatek

Xanadu

The goslings were growing up

When we arrived there were just a few rose beds, very unkempt

The garden is now very pleasant and colourful

The back porch and two dormers rebuilt

When Tallulah and Tess arrived, we made a great fuss of them

When we moved their house, Luly and Tess trotted behind the ark, squealing loudly

Tallulah giving Meriel a piggy-back!

Tallulah and Tess visited each other's sties

You look just like your mum!

Tess with some of the adopted piglets

Meriel feeding the runt from Tess's litter of twelve

When we got home, we backed the trailer right up to the stable door, and she rushed straight in to stand on the clean straw. We had been told to keep her in for a few days while we all got to know each other, so we made her comfortable with fresh hay and water, gave her a stroke, and went in to have supper. "We'll be back soon," I said.

We were sitting having a drink, when I suddenly saw her standing in the courtyard. "Quick, Rog! Somebody's let the cow out!"

We couldn't believe it, the stable door was still bolted and the front gate was locked. Emral Constellation was about 3 feet high at the shoulder and the bottom door of the stable was the same height, but she had jumped out. I got the halter. One look at it and her eyes started to roll. We managed to get the halter on, but she wouldn't budge. We coaxed, we pushed, we pulled, and finally we took the halter off, opened the stable door and gave her a sharp rap. In she went. Phew!

We decided to call her Jonquil. Jonquil the Jersey. Jonquil was supposedly in calf and she was 15 months old. She was very beautiful, quite bony, but not a bag of bones like poor Minnie. I spent many an hour training her to walk on a halter; cajoling her with titbits dangled in front of her nose. It was a long job, but she is an old hand now.

Jonnie arrived with a bit of a cough, and the vet thought it might be 'husk', which is a parasitic bronchitis caused by nematode worms that live in pasture. She had to have a course of injections which I undertook to give her. Up until now I had been the person that Jonnie knew best, and she trusted me. They say that a cow has a short memory, but our relationship has never recovered from that course of injections. If there is something unusual to be done to the animals, it is usually me who is the unpopular executor!

Of course Roger didn't have to milk Jonnie at this point as she had not yet had a calf, and we looked in some dismay at her tiny teats – only about half an inch long at the back section of her small udder, but by the end of the year she was clearly in calf. Her udder was swelling and she herself had filled out. She had grown into a lovely animal, and in a few months time Roger was going to have to start milking her. Once she has calved, a cow has to be milked or suckled every day if the milk supply is to be maintained. It is a skill that most people can acquire – but it takes months to acquire it. Normally, a cow is milked twice a day, once in the morning and once in the evening. Once you have chosen the times, it is important to milk her at the same times from then on.

Roger had been reading about the technique of milking: basically, you squeeze the teat between the first finger knuckle and the thumb, to stop the milk in the teat going back into the udder; and then progressively squeeze the teat with each finger from the first to the last, pushing the milk out of the teat. Sounds easy, but it's extremely difficult to begin with, especially with a young heifer.

Before Jonquil's first calf was due, Roger used to try practising his technique on her empty udder.

Her teats were so small that he could only get two fingers around her front teats, and barely one finger around the back teats. She didn't seem to mind him experimenting on her, but he had to stop practising, when Richard Morgan warned him that he might loosen a plug that stops infection going from the teat into the udder before calving.

Because Jonquil had already been artificially inseminated when we bought her, we knew the date when the calf was due. As the big day approached, her udder became absolutely enormous and rock hard. It was so large, that, when she walked along, she had to push her back legs apart, to avoid squashing the furry bag full of gallons of golden liquid. It must have felt like walking along trying to hold a medicine ball between your thighs. She herself was so enormous, that, a few weeks before she was due, we asked the Morgans to have a look at her, to see if we had been wrongly advised of her delivery date. They thought that her udder looked as if she was already to term, but her pin bones hadn't dropped (the bones on each side at the base of the tail), so she was not imminent. In fact to everyone's surprise she did go to term, by which time her udder was as hard as iron. We had been following the books, and clearly the amount of rolled grain recommended was too much for her, and we have never made the same mistake again.

She calved at the end of February 1995. We had her

in the cow shed at night for the last few days, and when she went into labour we were there. Being a heifer, and having what turned out to be a large bull calf, the labour was prolonged, and she finally delivered the calf lying down. When his feet and head, still covered in its foetal sac, appeared, it was the most wonderful and awe-inspiring event.

After she had presented the head, the delivery was straightforward, but Jonnie seemed exhausted, and lay without attending to the calf. I cleared the membranes from his nose and mouth, treated his umbilical cord with iodine, and gave him a rub with towels to dry him off, as it was a bitterly cold night, even in the shelter of the cow shed. We waited about fifteen minutes, but Jonnie still lay quietly, taking no notice of her new baby, who was starting to shiver. We were beginning to get a little worried about both mother and baby, so I carried him to her head and laid him beside her. After a few minutes she began to lick him. This was what we had been waiting for, but then she lay still again, so after another half an hour we carried him to the udder and put him on the teat. After considerable persuasion, he began to suck, and then Jonnie at last came to life; she stood up to make it easier for the calf to suckle, and turned her head to lick him vigorously. Now we knew all was well, and he was getting the vital colostrum. If the calf does not get colostrum within the first few hours of life, he is doomed. He needs at least 6 pints, and, if he is sucking strongly, he should get this in about twenty minutes. The calf was really tucking in, so, after watching them for a little longer, we left them alone, feeling very relieved and happy. It was a bull calf, and we called him Joshua.

When the calf is young, the cow is very protective and won't go anywhere without it – a cow can be very dangerous if she thinks her calf is threatened. Płatek is friendly with Jonnie, but he discovered a change in attitude when he sniffed the newly born calf – Jonnie butted him hard against the gate. He screamed, but seemed none the worse for wear, although he has never trusted Jonnie since.

Jonnie's udder was hard, red and shiny, and the calf was not noticeably softening it, although he was sucking well and looking healthy. After the first two days, when the calf would have had plenty of the rich colostrum (or beestings), Roger thought he must try and relieve the hardness of the udder by starting to milk her. It was with some trepidation that he tied Jonnie up at 7 a.m. on 2 March 1995 to milk her for the first time.

We hadn't yet built a stall in the cow shed, so Roger tied her up to the hay rack in the corner, and gave her some hay and some rolled grain. Even if a cow is bursting with milk so that it dribbles out of the teats, you can't squeeze it out of her unless she wants to give it to you (this is called letting the milk down), so he spent a long time washing and massaging her udder. Joshua was loose in the calf shed and kept trying to push Roger off his three-legged stool, but Jonnie seemed relaxed and ready to let him take the nectar.

Some people have told us that it takes only three to five minutes to completely empty a full udder. Half an hour later, Roger had this measly drop in the bottom of the bucket, and he said his hands were aching as if he'd shaken hands with a hundred Frank Brunos. He was bruised with Jonnie's constant kicking (she kicked forward to knock his hands off her teats) and, the worst indignity of all, showered with bits of excreta from her tail with which she lashed him throughout the whole depressing session. He had been so looking forward to carrying in a foaming bucket of our own milk, but the milking session had brought him to his lowest point since we had arrived at Upper Bridge Court.

However, he persevered. At this stage he was only trying to milk with one hand at a time. With the other hand, he would pull her tail forward between her legs, and then pull it backwards around one leg, thereby stopping it from lashing, and impeding her leg from kicking forward. But this didn't solve his problems – it wasn't long before, with a more violent kick, she managed not only to kick the bucket of milk but also ended up with her shitty foot in it!

Diana Palmer, whose Tamworth pigs had first won our hearts, also hand-milked her own Jersey cow, and Roger phoned her constantly to seek advice and support. She persuaded him of the benefits of an anti-kick bar – a large C-shaped bracket that hooks over the cow's back and in front of her hind leg. This has the effect of immobilising the leg and preventing her from kicking, and it is adjustable to suit different breeds. He bought one immediately. The first time he used it, he adjusted it too tightly, and poor Jonnie's leg was immobilised to the extent that it was paralysed and she fell over on top of him! He had to summon all his strength from his horizontal, squashed position to pull the bar off, so that Jonnie could stand up again and release him.

After much trial and error, Roger managed to adjust the anti-kick bar correctly and, by tying her tail to a bar behind her, he started to milk the teats on the near side with both hands. Milking the teats on the far side proved much more difficult, mainly because it was almost impossible to reach them under her colossal udder. He sawed a couple of inches off the legs of the milking stool but this didn't help. Furthermore, she would kick his hands off her teats on the far side because the anti-kick bar only works on one leg at a time. So he had to milk her on one side, then pick up the bucket and stool, untie her tail, remove the anti-kick bar, walk round the other side of her, set everything up again and milk that side. In fact, two calves and over 2,000 litres of milk later, he still milks her in this fashion.

Another early hazard was Jonquil's wish to urinate or excrete whilst being milked. This was not welcomed. After all, we were going to drink this milk, and when a cow urinates, a lot of liquid falls from a considerable height onto a hard surface and splashes all over the place. Roger would get some indication that this was about to happen, as she slowly arched her back. He could feel the muscles contract under his forehead (which was pressed against her flank), grabbed the milk bucket and held it on high. He used to shout at Jonnie when she did this, and she didn't like being shouted at at all! Her lovely eyes would widen anxiously. How many words animals recognise is a moot point, but whether it's sheep, pigs, horses or cattle, they do understand the tone of your voice. She rarely relieves herself during milking now.

During those early difficult days, Jonquil contracted mastitis, a serious infection of the udder. She had too much milk, both as a result of too much grain, and the fact that Roger's lack of milking experience couldn't get the milk out of her fast enough. She had mastitis in two of her quarters (the udder consists of four separate quarters, each with one teat). The vet gave us some antibiotics, every dose in a plastic syringe, which had to be administered by pushing the inch-long fine nozzle into each of her teat canals. This is a painful process. We didn't have a cattle crush to hold Jonnie still, and someone had suggested that we tie her back legs with shackles to stop her kicking whilst we discharged the syringe into her teat. This hurt her so much that she fell over, but whilst she was on her side we managed to give her the antibiotics. We cured the mastitis before it had got too serious, but the whole process was so traumatic that I was determined to find out more about homeopathic methods.

It took a lot of time and patience before Roger began to enjoy milking Jonquil. She got used to the routine, his hands became much stronger, and his technique developed. He now milks her in about five to ten minutes, and says it's a very therapeutic, calming experience, about which he waxes lyrical:

"There's no sound, other than Jonnie munching her hay or grain, the splash of the milk in the bucket and the birds singing around the courtyard. The open cow shed door frames a view along the little valley towards the Morgan's farm, lit by the rising sun. The fields, their colours of green, brown and yellow ever changing, depending on the season, dip gently towards the line of trees along the stream in the valley's floor. For a couple of weeks last autumn, whilst I sat on my milking stool in the silence and looked at the long shadows in the valley, a little robin came every day and perched near me in the cow shed. He clicked his tongue and I clicked back. He would stay a while, watching me, then fly off until the next day's return."

This is one of Roger's most treasured memories of the time we have been at Upper Bridge Court.

Although it now only takes him ten minutes to milk the cow, each milking session takes nearly two hours. Typically, starting at 6 a.m., he separates the cream and milk, which has been standing since yesterday's milking, and washes up all the pans ready for today's milk. Then at 6.30 a.m. he goes out, armed with the milk bucket and a bucket of hot water to the cow shed. Jonquil is always grazing in the pasture except when it's very cold, windy and wet, so he has to bring her in, tie her up, wash her udder and his hands, and milk her at about 7 a.m. Next, he takes the milk indoors, pours it through a filter into the cream-setting pan, washes everything up, and then goes outside again to take her back to the pasture. By now, it's nearly 8 a.m., but it usually takes longer because for most of the year there is a calf who has to be moved to and fro with her.

Roger was prepared to go through this routine

twice a day but Diana Palmer told him how to avoid this. For the first six weeks after the calf's birth, the cow has a lot of milk, the calf doesn't take much, so she has to be milked twice a day to avoid mastitis and to maintain the supply of milk. After this, the calf can be taken away from the cow for twelve hours overnight, and the cow milked once a day, in the morning, before reuniting them.

This is a big adjustment to make in the feeding habits of a six-week-old calf. The first time we did it, not only did the cow and the calf cry heart-breakingly across the farm for several nights, but the calf would rush to Jonnie in the morning and gorge himself on milk. He then proceeded to have diarrhoea, or scour, very badly. This put him off milk for a few days, so Jonnie developed the medicine ball between her legs once more, and Roger had to milk her twice a day again, until the calf was better.

We found it quite astonishing how the volume of milk Jonquil produced was closely related to how much food and drink she had had in the previous twenty-four hours. If her water supply had dried up, or, being a very fussy eater, she didn't like a particular bale of hay, the next day her milk supply would drop off drastically.

The other thing that dramatically affects her milk supply is the presence of strangers. In 1996 we were contacted by Touch Productions, who suggested making a documentary involving our life at Upper Bridge Court. When the film crew were filming the milking sequence, Jonnie demonstrated this idiosyncrasy; as she rounded the corner from the barn to come into the cow shed, she was confronted by five people (who probably didn't smell quite right), bright lights and whirring cameras. She immediately reacted by arching her back and passing a large cow pat. Then she took two paces forward, arched her back again, and repeated the performance. She proceeded to take the understandable attitude of "If you think I'm going to stand here in front of all these people and have my teats squeezed and give you lots of milk you've got another think coming." There was Roger, milking in front of potentially millions of people, trying to show how expert he was, and all he had to show for it was a small cupful of milk. Jonnie had not 'let her milk down' – on the other hand, she had a very satisfied look on her face!

What an amazing animal a cow is. All you do is put grass or hay and a little rolled grain in one end, and out of the other comes the brown stuff with which she manures the land directly, and the white stuff which is delicious to drink or can be converted quite simply into several other nutritious foods. Jonquil is a most amiable animal with lovely sweet breath and the patience of Job. She creates a lot of work but the rewards from the produce and the pleasure are more than worth the effort – so Roger assures me!

I feel very proud of Roger's achievements with Jonnie, because although we both enjoy conquering new fields, there are some things I wouldn't have the courage to embark on. I am reminded of the days when Roger learned to sail a dinghy. He first went off to adult swimming classes, and, having learned to swim relatively late in life, he took a course in dinghy sailing at the Queen Mary Sailing Club, near Heathrow, and bought his own dinghy during the course. He got hooked on conquering the elements, on the sensation of natural power; sailing in a strong wind with the spinnaker billowing; the crew at full stretch on the trapeze wire; the boat planing on top of the water. He sailed year round, when the spinnaker pole freezes to the mast, when the wet ropes had frozen so stiff on the reach you couldn't pull them through the pulleys to adjust the sail. Once he capsized in a snowstorm – and he loved every minute of it.

He used to take his children to Rock, on the Camel Estuary in Cornwall, and race the dinghy from the club. One wet and windy day, Lesley had joined them and had accompanied Roger early in the morning to watch the day's race. He was placed well in the race series, and, if he did well in the race, he could win the cup. Roger's crew did not turn up in time – he turned to the unsuspecting Lesley and commanded: "Put the trapeze harness and life jacket on." She'd been in a dinghy before but had never raced or been on a trapeze. They approached the starting line just in time, and Roger managed to give her one instruction: "All you have to do is keep the mast vertical at all times."

It's essential that the helm and the crew are as one. Although Roger had done well all week with his regular crew, they had not kept the mast quite vertical – but Lesley obeyed Roger's instruction to the letter. He says he will never forget her horizontal body hanging from the trapeze wire just above the surface of the sea, being soaked by wave after wave, shaking the water from her tousled hair between each drenching. And did they plane! They won by miles and with it the series cup. I don't think I would have been so brave.

Jonnie's first calf, Joshua, was a pure Jersey bull. Jersey beef is good meat but is not popular to eat, because the fat is rather yellow and doesn't look wholesome on the butcher's slab. We therefore decided, as soon as he was born, that we would slaughter Joshua when he was six months old, and keep the beef for ourselves. If she had had a heifer, we could have sold the calf as a milker.

Slaughtering Joshua was very hard to do. He was the first animal to go to the abattoir since we had taken Compost. That was tough, but sheep are the least friendly of all farm animals, whereas we had helped Josh into the world, put him on the teat, and handled him once or twice a day at milking times.

Joshua was a real character and quite a handful. He was still 'entire' (he had not been castrated), and Jersey bulls have a reputation of being the most difficult of all bulls. He often led us a merry dance when we were trying to catch him, waiting until we were within inches of him before galloping off with his eyes rolling wickedly. Brian Morgan gave us a sound piece of advice: "Take the calf to the cow shed and the cow will follow." He didn't tell us how to catch the calf. We had trained Jonnie to walk on a halter and she normally lets us walk up to her and put it on, but not Joshua! From a few days old he was extremely agile and could run like the wind. We used to try to drive him into a corner of the field, using hurdles to make a temporary pen in which to trap him. Often it would take fifteen minutes to catch him and sometimes it took both of us to do it. As he got older, and started to eat some rolled grain, he could be tempted, and became used to the routine – but he liked to remind Roger at regular intervals that the chase was part of the routine as well! Perversely, if the sun was shining, he was a lovely sight, galloping full tilt around the field, his tail streaming horizontally behind him, scattering the sheep in all directions. If it was chucking it down, he didn't look quite so beautiful and Roger would call him all the names under the sun.

Joshua was growing big, and it wouldn't be long before his games might become dangerous. The day that we had tried to put off had arrived. We endeavour to make the procedure as stress free as possible. The abattoir is half an hour away, and we telephone beforehand to establish a time when the animals can go straight through, rather than being penned up at the abattoir when they arrive. Joshua hadn't been in the trailer before and he took a lot of coaxing and pushing, with Jonnie watching through the gate and mooing plaintively. I couldn't face any more, and once Josh was in the trailer, I abandoned Roger, who was feeling pretty low when they arrived at the abattoir. Fortunately there was no delay: Roger went straight to the unloading bay, and Joshua walked out of sight to his death quite calmly.

Jonnie was already in calf when we bought her, but now we had to arrange to get her in calf again, in order to maintain the milk supply. We enquired about taking her to a bull, but it would be extremely expensive, and difficult to arrange with the milking routine and the suckling calf. Because it is not easy to sell Jersey meat, we decided it would be safer to inseminate Jonnie from another breed, so that we could grow the calf on and get a good price for the meat. A Jersey is a very small cow, so the bull could not be from a large breed, and we chose an Aberdeen Angus.

Jerseys are notoriously difficult to inseminate, and it took two attempts before it was successful. The period of oestrus recurs every twenty-one days or so, lasts for about twenty-four hours, and she must be inseminated during that brief time. It is vital to get the timing right, which is not easy with a single cow. The clue that she is on heat is that she will try mounting another cow. This is called 'bulling'. We don't have another cow, but fortunately Jonnie will mount anything that moves: it might be her calf, or it might be you, so it's best not to turn your back or bend over in front of her – it's not much fun having 300 kilos of cow clambering onto your back.

When you are confident that the cow is in oestrus, you call the artificial insemination service who will come within hours to inseminate her. The process is very efficient: you choose the sire from the company's sperm bank of pedigree, tested bulls; a skilled operator comes to the farm with the 'straw' (the tube holding the sperm); and inserts it manually into the cow's uterus. After that there is nothing to do but wait and see if she is in calf.

We were privileged to have witnessed the birth of Joshua, but Jonnie's second delivery was apparently much quicker and easier, both because it was a smaller calf and because she was now a 'first calf heifer'. One day she was very pregnant, and the next, when Roger went to feed her in the field, he did a double take – a calf was standing next to her, suckling vigorously. There was no other evidence of the birth.

We called Jonnie's second calf Jake. We had Jake castrated, so that he would be easier to manage than a bull, and could therefore be kept until he was eighteen months to two years old before being sold for meat. The vet came and did a very skilled and lightning job of the castration when Jake was five weeks old; after a local anaesthetic, he seemed almost unaware that anything was happening, and appeared to suffer no discomfort afterwards. I couldn't help thinking of poor Płatek who had the most traumatic and bloody experience when he had suffered the same indignity.

When the time came for Roger to start milking only once a day, we wanted to prevent Jake from being upset by drinking too much milk, as Josh had been, so, instead of shutting him in all night, we initially separated him from the cow for only six hours, by bringing him in from the pasture at midnight. Over the next couple of weeks, Roger gradually brought this time forward to 6 p.m., which prevented the scouring and its complications, but didn't stop the plaintive mooing.

Jonnie will have to be rested for two months before calving again, so not only does Roger have to stop milking, but we also have to stop the calf suckling her. We don't have space to put him in another field so we intend to clip a sort of knuckle-duster to his nose which allows him to graze and drink but will make the cow move away if he tries to suckle her. Hopefully, by then, he will not be suckling that much and it won't be too much of a trial for either of them.

1994 had been the year of our big expansion: the year we acquired the pigs, the sheep, the cow, the horse and the hens. In retrospect it might have been wiser to wait until we were a little more prepared. As it was, we had to learn most things as we went along. There was always a job to be done in a hurry: a shelter to build; a fence to mend; equipment to buy. But it seemed right at the time, and we have no regrets – except that we had almost abandoned work on the house!

There is never enough time to do everything that needs to be done. Our financial situation demands that we do most of the work on the house and the farm ourselves, but the daily routine jobs of feeding and caring for the stock leave only a few hours to focus on other projects. Roger spent thirty years in a very structured environment at IBM, and it is difficult for him to be reconciled to the fact that although the days are always busy with important activities, they are not always the activities we planned: a sick animal; a water or electricity cut; someone coming to look at or buy stock; the weather and endless other factors will suddenly take precedence.

Roger tries to start the day at 5 a.m., when he feeds the stock and does the milking. He is very scientific about his round, as he has to carry bales of straw and hay, 25-kilo bags of pig food, grain for the poultry, halters for the cow, the calf and the horse, and sometimes water as well. He uses a yoke that Andrea and Mark bought him for his birthday so that he can carry things in his hands and on his shoulders.

I certainly don't start the day at 5 a.m. unless there is some emergency, but I use the time before breakfast to do research on animal husbandry, welfare, rules and regulations. There are endless forms to fill out, records to keep, identification, registration, and movement licences to apply for. For farmers with large herds and flocks it is a mammoth and confusing task. After breakfast I do all the mucking out, and Roger does routine jobs that have come to the forefront such as rolling grain, plucking and dressing hens or geese, making bread and butter, repairing a fence, etc. Between us we shop for stores and organic feed, and, according to the time of year, identify young stock with tattoos or tags, deliver the new-born, do the shearing, trim hooves, take animals for breeding or slaughter, and move the hens, sheep, pigs and cattle to new grazing. Sometimes, such as at harvest time, we are busy from dawn until dusk. The vegetable garden and the garden are also my responsibility. So there is not much time for work on the house!

We had originally decided that we would wait until we had got the house into reasonably good shape, and then get some domestic help, so that I would have more time to spend on other matters. However, this date appeared to be continually receding, and so we advertised in the *Penta Paper* for some help in the house. It was an agreeable surprise to get several replies, but we chose a very nice lady called Margaret, who assured us that she could put up with the dust and the unfinished state of the house. She has been true to her word, and been a wonderful help to me – but I think she is longing as much as we are for the day when the wiring is finished, the decorating is done, and the carpets are laid!

Roger has been rewiring the house for over a year, but the farm takes so much time now, that he can only manage a few hours a week on this mammoth job (sometimes not even that), and until the wiring is finished, we can't finish mending the floor boards, decorate, or fit the carpets. We're getting there gradually – it's just that Roger's one year plan to get the house ship-shape is taking five years to implement!

The Development

Ye rigid Ploughmen! Bear in mind
Your labour is for future hours.
Advance! Spare not! Nor look behind!
Plough deep and straight with all your powers!

Richard Henry Horne

Our complement of farm animals was growing fast, and my job was to keep up to date with learning how to feed and care for them. I had now been on several courses run by the ATB (Agricultural Training Board), for pig handling, for sheep handling, for lambing, for calving, for mole control, and for pond management, but the longest course I had been on was a year's equestrian course, one day a week, at the Holme Lacey College of Agriculture, near Hereford.

When I was growing up, my sister Gil and I went to boarding school, and we spent the holidays at various places arranged by my mother – our parents lived in Malaya, where I was born. We spent several years at

Gussage All Saints, in Dorset, where I learned to ride, joined the pony club, and won a few rosettes at gymkhanas. But my equestrian knowledge was too little and too rusty, and so I drove into Holme Lacey once a week to learn how to feed, care for and manage a horse. I also got several hours of riding a day, of a rather more advanced standard than I would have liked, and collected a few bruises to show for it! I had wanted a horse before we came to Upper Bridge Court, but, when we arrived, the house had taken precedence, and none of the outbuildings was in a fit state to stable a horse.

Now that we had become farmers instead of retiring, the desired horse had metamorphosed into a draught horse to work on the land. I still wanted to ride, so the search was on for an animal that would fulfil both criteria.

The search was long, the most difficult of all our endeavours to find an animal. We initially thought that a Welsh cob would suit our needs. They are very pretty, hardy animals, and usually go well in harness. However, when we went to look at some, it was apparent that they were too small for our needs, and would not be strong enough to pull the heavy loads we had in mind. We eventually heard of a six-year-old Dales-cross gelding, who was being used in a riding school nearby, and had also been broken to harness. Roger and I went to see him one spring morning in 1994, and he looked a sturdy animal. Jet, as he was called, was black, still with his shaggy winter coat, and very muddy. We liked the look of him, and arranged that I should come back and take him out for a ride. I wanted to get a second opinion, so I rang up my cousin Sally.

On the day that we moved to Upper Bridge Court, a young woman had appeared on the lawn with a baby in her arms.

"You probably don't remember me, but you were at my wedding," she said to Roger. It was my cousin, Sally Jones. The only time we had met her was at her wedding in Hampshire in 1989, at which time she and her husband John, both lawyers, lived and worked in Bristol. John was born in the village, on his parent's farm, and, unknown to us, he and Sally had moved there shortly before our own arrival here. She had always loved horses, and had worked with them all her life, and now had two of her own.

Sally and I went to see Jet, all prepared in our riding togs, and Sally was lent another horse to ride. Jet was easy to ride, but seemed reluctant to be handled, and we arranged that he should come to us on trial for four weeks.

I now had to prepare the stable, which was full of rubbish and had been used as a wood shed. I had to lug all the logs out and pile them into another disused shed. The assortment of objects that I crammed into dustbins had to be seen to be believed – they ranged from old boots to ancient harness, too rotten to be of any use. Roger had to drop his other work again to make a stable door and frame, which he copied from the old broken one, and made a brilliant job of it. We got the fittings made up by Peter Crownshaw, exactly as they would have been long ago. Roger showed him an old broken hinge strap which we assumed was original, and Peter copied this, and also designed some simple iron bolts, and made the nails for fixing the fittings to the door.

We needed some secure fencing in the paddock, so Roger telephoned David Griffiths to see if he could give us some help. He was too busy, so we thought we would contact Brian and Richard Morgan who had helped us install the oil tank at the beginning of the year. Richard said he would be pleased to do it, and came over a few days later with a post hammer attached to the back of his tractor. The hammer is a 12-foot-long arm with a heavy weight on the end, on the underside of which is a square metal plate. Having made a small deep hole in the ground with a heavy iron stake, Roger's job was to hold each post vertically, with its point in the hole, while Richard manoeuvred the tractor and positioned the hammer so that the square metal plate rested on top of the post. Richard would then raise the hammer hydraulically and let it fall. At first, he would raise the hammer a little whilst they made sure the post was vertical, and then raise it higher to give the post several hefty clouts.

The gate posts are about 8 inches in diameter, and they are inserted first, in order to hang the 12-foot-wide gate. Next, the end posts are positioned, and the pig netting is stretched from them to the gate posts. The netting is stapled at one end, pulled taught with the tractor and then stapled at the other end. This gives a straight line of netting to guide the position of the smaller intermediate posts, which can be hammered in more easily. Finally, the netting is stapled to the intermediate posts and the gate is hung. All in all, 50 metres of fencing with a gate took only a few hours.

Although this was the second time Roger and Richard had met, it was the first time they had talked and got to know each other. Apparently they covered a lot of topics and got on easily together despite their disparate backgrounds and a fifteen-year age gap. Richard was very interested in what we were trying to do and was very helpful and supportive. Most generously, he offered to help with the farm jobs that we were not equipped to handle, and this offer was gratefully accepted. We hope that, as time goes by, and as we continue to learn, we will be able to do more jobs ourselves, but unless we invest in a tractor and equipment, we will always need some help to manage even our relatively small patch of land. Meanwhile, a sturdy fence had been erected for our new horse.

I was very excited the evening Jet walked down the ramp of the horse box, and was led into his new stable. We had decided to keep him in at night for a few days, so that we could get to know each other, and the next morning, I went into the stable with the head collar, to take him out to pasture and to let him find his way around. But Jet had other ideas; he barged me against the wall, and threw his head around. This was not like the riding-school horses I had been working with at Holme Lacey, and he made me rather nervous, which of course he was aware of. However, I got the head collar on, and led him out to the paddock. He walked beside me as good as gold, and I decided my fears had been unjustified, and that we would soon get to know each other. Jet loved his new field, lush with ungrazed spring grass, and he galloped around the perimeter before deciding to have a good roll. I leaned on the fence and watched him, so happy to have my own horse at last, and to see him in our paddock. Roger came out and found me laughing with pleasure.

When I went to bring Jet in that evening, I took a bucket of titbits, and called his name. He cantered towards me, and willingly let me put the head collar on. I gave him his reward, and made a fuss of him before leading him back to the stable. I tied him up outside so that I could give him a good brush – he had arrived as muddy as the day we first saw him. But now the trouble began in earnest; as soon as I tried to groom him, Jet started barging and pushing me, especially if I went near his belly. When I tried to pick his feet up, he kicked out immediately. I didn't persevere for long, I didn't have the confidence, so I phoned Sally and asked if she would come over and see what she could do. Sally had no more success than I, and I thought I should get another opinion: I asked a riding-school instructress, who also broke horses, to come and have a look at Jet. It was some comfort to me that Jet behaved even worse with this lady, rearing up when she tried to pick up his feet. Her conclusion was, that as he had been gelded late, at the age of four, he was 'riggy', that is to say, he still had some of the aggressive behaviour of a stallion. She didn't think that Jet was the horse for someone like me. I had had Jet for two weeks now. In the paddock he was as good as gold. He would follow me around when I was working in the paddock; if I was picking up droppings, he would walk ahead to the next pile and stand beside it. He was very easy to catch and to lead – but wouldn't let me groom him. He also barged Roger around if he went into his stable. We reluctantly concluded that we didn't want to continue to do battle with Jet, and that he needed a more experienced handler. So Jet went home, and the search began again.

We got in touch with the Heavy Horse Society, and they gave us several horses to follow up. One of them was a large, handsome four-year-old Percheron gelding called William, from a Percheron stable in Staffordshire. He was a lovely, dapple-grey animal, but I thought he was a bit too lively for me (after my experience with Jet, I was looking for an amiable beast), and he had not yet been trained to harness.

The next horse we heard about was a seven-year-old, sixteen-hand Shire gelding, also from Staffordshire. Roger and I went to see him in his field. He was a huge gentle beast, but had not been broken to ride. His name was John, black with two white socks – if he had had four white socks he would have been beyond our price bracket. We were very taken with him, and arranged to return and try him out.

The manager of the Percheron stable had given us the name of a horse dealer called George Smith, whom he described as, "knowing more about horses than anyone else in the country", and George agreed to come with us to try out Big John. Unfortunately Big John caught a chill, and it was several weeks before we could return to try him out. He had been groomed until he was shining, and all his harness was gleaming as well. We did some snigging, or hauling logs, with him, and he behaved perfectly. Our hopes were high, but now I had to see if he was easy to ride. Well, he wasn't easy to ride, and seemed very sluggish. The stable girl said that it was probably because he had only been ridden bareback, so she undertook to liven him up a bit. Oh dear! He bolted with her, and she came off, falling heavily on her shoulder. She didn't want to upset the sale, and insisted it was nothing, but she looked very pale.

George had watched the proceedings without comment, but on the way home he advised us against buying Big John, and said he thought he knew of a horse that would suit us well. Unfortunately his owner was seriously ill with cancer, and although the horse was therefore now out to grass, his wife didn't want to sell him under the present circumstances. George had broken the horse to harness when he was younger, and had sold him to his present owner. He was a six-year-old cob gelding called Troy. George took us to see him on our way home. Troy looked very small compared to Big John. He was not quite fifteen hands high, black, with four white socks and a white blaze. Stocky and strongly built, he looked like a Shire-cross. He had a fine moustache, which was a feature of the Dales' side of his ancestry. We liked him, but after all, he wasn't available at present, and there was no way of telling when he would be. So we continued our search.

A few weeks later, we heard of another Shire, a

mare called Sheba, with foal at foot. The farm was at Much Marcle, not far from Holme Lacey, and one of the instructors from my equestrian course came with us to try Sheba out. The farmer had gone to a lot of trouble to borrow some agricultural equipment, so that we could work with Sheba. If we had had the experience that we have now, we probably would have bought her; she was kind and willing, but a bit too ongoing for us, although it took several days of agonising before we came to that decision. She had to be held back strongly, which can be a good thing in the right hands, but not for beginners.

We saw a chestnut cob who was too small, but just wonderful to handle. We were all set to go and look at him again when his owner decided she couldn't bear to part with him! We went to see a 'schoolmaster' (a very well-mannered, well-trained horse) in Abergavenny, who turned out to be a ten-year-old stallion with a wall eye. We were offered a horse on loan, who pulled gypsy caravans for holiday makers in the summer. Gypsy looked about twenty-two years old, very bony and not too steady on his pins. We were to pay for the privilege of looking after him. Well, we're green, but not that green! We looked at several horses 'on paper', some of which looked as if they might suit us, but all of which were beyond our price limit. We looked at a Shire mare with a foal, at Craven Arms, who was living wild and the owner couldn't catch her. There were a lot of Shires and Percherons on the farm, most of which were unbroken, and were being sold off because the owner's father had died, and the horses were no longer used. It was sad to see all these wonderful animals no longer wanted. Once the farm had been run by horse power, and there were sheds full of mouldering tack, too rotten to salvage. We bought a small horse plough from the pile of discarded implements, but a plough needs two horses to pull it, and we only have it for old times' sake.

One evening, when we were going to supper at Kington, we saw a Shire horse in a field nearby. Enquiries brought us to the owner, Peter Banks, who was planning to set up a heavy horse centre in Kington. He was willing to sell the horse we had seen, who was a Shire mare called Blossom, and trained to ride and to harness. She was about ten years old, and over sixteen hands high. Roger and I set forth again, and we spent the morning working with Blossom, who was very easy to handle. I arranged to come back and ride her the following day. We didn't anticipate any problems, as Peter rode her regularly. Peter's assistant, Simon, accompanied me on the ride on his own Shire gelding, Hector. Hector was a big softy, the most docile of all the big heavy horses that I had ever met – or have met since. We had a pleasant easy ride, and I was feeling elated, until we met a car coming down the steep narrow lane which we were climbing on horseback. There was no room to pass, so the car had to back up. However, it had a slipping clutch, and couldn't make any headway on the steep hill. It is dangerous for heavy horses to go down a very steep tarmacked road, so Simon and I dismounted, and I held the horses while Simon pushed the car back up the hill to the nearest passing point. Simon then leaped acrobatically on to the back of the gangly Hector, but, try as I might, I couldn't manage to get onto Blossom without a leg-up from Simon!

Peter and Simon said that they would give us some lessons in using agricultural implements, so that we could get off to a good start with Blossom. Peter was also very interested to hear about the Shires and Percherons which were being sold off at Craven Arms, and subsequently bought some of them, which we were extremely pleased about. Blossom was perfect in every way, except that I was unhappy about riding a horse out in the country, when I couldn't get on her back without help – there were gates to open and other possible reasons for dismounting – but she was easily the best horse we had seen. We were still discussing it when we had a telephone call from George Smith. Sadly, Troy's owner had died, but the horse was now available.

We saw Troy for the second time on 31 May 1994. We drove him to a sledge, and I also rode him. We had no doubts whatsoever – here, at last, was our horse. George proposed taking Troy for two weeks to get him fit and back into harness, and then he would bring him to Upper Bridge Court. Troy arrived on 23 July, and he has been the most wonderful animal we could possibly have hoped for, kind and willing, but with a mind of his own, a real character.

So did this horse excel a common one
In shape, in courage, colour, pace and bone,
Round-hoof'd, short jointed, fetlocks shag and
long,
Broad breast, full eye, small head and nostril wide,
High crest, short ears, straight legs and passing
strong,
Thin mane, thick tail, broad buttock, tender hide:
Look, what a horse should have he did not lack . . .

William Shakespeare

While we were searching for a horse, I had been taking driving lessons from an expert lady called Sarah Wildy. Sarah drove and showed ponies, and although they were very well-behaved and well-trained, they soon realised that a novice was holding the reins. However, I improved, and the time came when Sarah entrusted me on the roads. All went well, and she came to Upper Bridge Court one day to put Troy in the trap with me for the first time. Troy had his own driving harness which we had bought from George Smith, and we had also had a small trap made for exercising him. Sarah was surprised how light Troy's mouth was (he doesn't like a tight rein), and said she realised why she was always having to tell me to hold her little ponies on a harder rein. Troy went well, and I was given the official seal of approval.

During our long search for the right horse, we had been keeping our eye on the farm sales, for horse-drawn equipment and tack. Roger had recently bought a scythe from a Mr Brick who, before he retired, worked on a large farm where he used to work draught horses from dawn to dusk. When we saw some heavy-horse harness in a sale near Haverfordwest, Roger asked Mr Brick if he would accompany him so that he could capitalise on Mr Brick's experience and expertise. He willingly agreed and they travelled to the sale together, returning with a complete set of heavy-horse harness. At this point, we hadn't bought Troy, so we were very lucky that the harness fitted him, as it wouldn't have fitted a larger draught horse.

Heavy horses are immensely strong, but, if they're very tall, the power tends to lift an agricultural implement, such as a plough, off the ground rather than pulling it through the earth. Today, most draught horses are bred for showing, and being tall has become an important feature which is encouraged. In the days when working horses were used on farms, draught horses were crossed with a heavy cob to produce a strong horse with shorter legs, called a half leg or a vanner.

Troy is of this ilk. Shire and Yorkshire Dale appear to be the main ingredients of his ancestry, although his mother was a coloured cob. The Yorkshire Dale was known as the cart horse of the fells, because they are so strong and sturdy, although relatively small. Troy is only 14.2 hands, but he weighs about 500 kilos.

When we bought Troy from George Smith, we also bought from him a flat-bed trolley, or dray, with what transpired to be Morris Minor wheels. We'd also by now acquired a spike harrow from a farm sale. We contacted Peter Banks, the owner of Blossom, to see if he was still willing to let Simon give us some instruction in using horse-drawn implements. It transpired that Simon was no longer working for Peter, but we managed to track him down through his father, who was the landlord of a local pub. Simon agreed to give us some instruction in return for letting his Shire horse, Hector, graze here while he was looking for new pasture. He gave us some invaluable help, first in showing us how to tack up with working harness, and also in how to make some modifications to the brackets on the dray. Luckily, the old harness fitted Troy well, and we were able to start our first lesson immediately, driving the heavy dray in full harness, and working in traces with the spike harrow. Like any new subject we learned a lot – only a fraction of what there is to know, but enough for us to work Troy ourselves and learn by our own mistakes. We couldn't have done it without a horse of Troy's nature. He is truly a gentle giant and loves working between shafts or in traces.

In due course, we set forth on our first job, collecting stones from under the hedgerows around our fields. I needed these large stones, as I had undertaken the task of building and repairing stone walls, and we use the smaller ones in the gateways, and on the track to the fields behind the barn. Stones come to the surface when the land is cultivated and the farmer of the day would usually carry them to the field margins. Troy had obviously worked in shafts a lot, and was very obedient and willing. It didn't appear to be hard work for him, although the dray was well loaded with huge stones, but Roger had to walk around the field margins, lifting the stones onto the dray whilst I did the driving! Płatek gets intensely excited when we work Troy, and leaps onto the dray as soon as he sees us tacking up. He stands beside me looking like a canine Charlton Heston, or runs in circles around the moving dray, narrowly missing Troy's trotting feet every time he passes under his nose.

Troy was also very well schooled in harrowing the land. By now, we had bought a variety of harrows privately or at farm sales. Instead of shafts, two long chains (the traces) are hooked to the horse's collar and to the ends of a bar behind his back legs, wide enough to prevent the chains touching the horse's feet. The bar, called a lantry, has a hook in the middle to which the harrows are attached. We tried the chain harrow first, to aerate the paddock and spread out any heaps of horse dung. This didn't need much accuracy on the part of the horse or the driver and Roger was pleased with the result, but working Troy in traces means walking on uneven ground, at the horse's pace, level with his hind quarters, holding the reins, or lines, that control the bit, and being careful not to harrow your own feet. It was hard work, but he found that feeling Troy's tremendous power at work was very exhilarating.

Roger says he has always had an uplifting feeling from using natural power. He once bought his children fighting kites for Christmas. The kites had a single control line but, by pulling it hard, the kite would zoom across the sky in the direction that it was pointing at the time. I believe they are called fighting kites because in some countries, particularly India, by sticking something abrasive on the control line just below the kite, it is possible to cross your line with that of your opponent and cut his kite free, thereby winning the contest. They didn't try fighting with their kites, but Roger remembers vividly the exhilarating feeling as the kite, in a strong wind, tries to lift you off the ground.

After the relatively easy introduction of harrowing the paddock, Troy and Roger attempted to harrow about one and a half acres with spring tines, in preparation for sowing wheat. A spring tine harrow has several circular springs or tines, each of which has a pointed blade that sticks forward in the ground. There is a lever to adjust the depth of the tines in the soil. This was hard work, but Troy appeared to enjoy it. Roger planned his route so that the harrowing pattern covered the whole area, whilst keeping the overlap to a minimum. Troy was very good at following alongside the last pass of the harrows, so that the harrow tracks neither overlapped nor left gaps.

The field is not quite flat but by no stretch of the imagination is the slope steep. On the uphill section, Troy always stopped several times, and wouldn't start again without repeated requests, but within ten seconds he would start again of his own accord. Roger soon realised that he was just having a blow, as he does on a steep hill if I am riding him. Troy also likes to run at the turn into the hill, so he can launch himself at the hardest part; Roger then has to run much faster on a longer path to keep up with him!

It took a couple of hours to harrow the one-and-a-half-acre field, and Troy and Roger were both in a fine sweat long before they'd finished. Now and again they would have a break and share an apple. There is something special about standing next to Troy, his neck and flank wet with sweat, vaporising in a small cloud in the warm autumn sunshine. It is good to take time to admire the neat line of damp rich soil behind the harrows, and the rolling Herefordshire hills behind. Tractors have lots of advantages, but they can't better this.

We've now bought a small tipping cart with large wooden wheels, which we've so far used only for carting dead docks' heads from the fields. It's not as roomy as the dray, but it's much more manoeuvrable and crosses the ground more smoothly. Roger carries all the food and straw to the animals in the winter as part of the twice daily feeding routine, but, as the daily load increases, it may be better to set up small shelters near the animals, and cart all the stuff out with Troy once a week. We'll probably try this next winter.

Troy is also clearly experienced in pulling logs, called snigging or tushing. Traces are used, but a chain is hooked from the lantry and looped around the end of a fallen tree trunk or log. We needed to move a 20-foot-long Scots Pine, that had come down in a gale, in the wood where some of the pigs were living. Horses don't as a rule like or even tolerate pigs, but Troy will now touch noses with them through the fence. However, we would soon be out of control if we took Troy into the wood with the pigs running round his feet, so, with Troy standing outside the gate, we tied a rope to the tree trunk, passed it under the gate, and then tied the other end to the lantry. Roger had tried to move this tree trunk to line it up with the rope but it was too heavy to budge an inch.

"Gidup Troy boy." Troy moved forward and didn't even alter his stride as the rope tightened. The tree trunk rolled into line, and then obediently followed the rope up the slight slope and out of the wood. I managed to open the gate at the right moment for the log to slide through, warily keeping an eye on the pigs.

We've done some more snigging since then, after pollarding the oak tree, and Troy regularly pulls the pig arks and hen houses when we move the animals from strip to strip. He's invaluable at these times, because the land is often too wet to use a four-track vehicle, and, if the pigs have been routing the ground up for the last six months, even a tractor may have some problems.

Troy's biggest job so far has been bringing in the straw bales from last year's harvest. Earlier in the year, Richard and Brian had brought in the hay bales. We had gone out for supper, rain was forecast for the morning, so they came over and started loading the trailer in the field and unloading it in the barn. When we came home at about ten o'clock, the first thing we noticed was that the barn doors were wide open, and there was a wonderful smell of new-mown hay. Roger and I changed quickly and gave them a hand, and the job was done in another hour.

During the harvest the weather broke before we had finished. There was too much to be done and not enough dry weather to do it in. Brian and Richard had baled our straw, but were too busy with their own harvest to bring the bales in. Rain was again forecast, and we needed to get the straw in before it got wet. Troy brought it all in for us. We toiled for hours, backwards and forward to the barn with twenty-five bales piled four-layers-high on the dray. He stood impatiently while we loaded them, then carried the tottering load across the fields, into the lane, into the courtyard, and finally into the barn. There he waited whilst the bales were unloaded and stacked. We had to make about ten journeys, opening and shutting three gates each time. When rain threatens, we must carry on until the last bale is safely brought in, working, if necessary, after darkness falls. Troy was heaving and sweating before we had finished, and sometimes had to stop to draw breath, but he was willing to the last. I can well believe the stories of horses dropping in their tracks. Well, we would never work our Troy like that, but he would give of his best to the end.

I would drive Troy up to the barn, then Roger would take his head and encourage him as far as possible into the barn, so that we could throw the bales onto the stack. There is a slight rise into the barn, and the floor is made of large stone flags, so it is difficult for Troy to get a grip with his steel shoes. Although he was getting very tired, he made a better job of it each time. What he hated was reversing the big dray out of the barn, with Roger trying to steer from his head. We've now had the broken back doors of the barn replaced, so next year we'll be able to drive the dray in, unload it, and then drive straight out of the back.

Roger had never had anything to do with horses, let alone working one in harness or 'gears', but now he has worked with Troy for over eighteen months, they understand each other a lot better and work well as a team. We haven't time at the moment to work Troy as much as we would all like, but next spring we're going to try him out on a single-horse mower with a 2-foot-6-inch blade and a seat on the back for the driver. There's a lot more work waiting to be done with Troy. It's a wonderful sense of achievement to harness his power to work our land, and all that power comes from grass and hay, with the odd carrot, apple, or cup of rolled oats thrown in – for being a good boy.

On Christmas Eve, we harness Troy in the trap and take some small presents to our neighbours. The dogs start to get excited as soon as we begin to harness up – they will run beside the trap all the way. It's very peaceful outside, no-one is working, and the fields and lanes are quiet. Troy's hooves ring on the frosty ground, and he steps out with a will, his head held high and his mane and tail streaming in the wind. He looks his best in harness, and we love to sit behind him, love to see his strong hindquarters working, love the smell of his warm body steaming in the cold air.

Last Christmas Eve was a beautiful clear winter's

day and, as we drove along the driveway to David Griffiths' farm, we could see the River Wye meandering through the fields in the valley below, and Hay-on-Wye nestling beneath the Black Mountains, silhouetted against the blue sky. We were pretty cold by the end of the round, and at our last port of call (Walter and Heather Williams, just below Upper Bridge Court), we tied Troy up, and accepted some liquid hospitality. But Troy had just seen a frightening dragon (a red tractor) in the Morgans' yard, and was very spikey and fired up, so while Heather and I sat by the fire indoors with a Christmas sherry, Walter kept Roger company outside as he hung on to the prancing steed, at the same time managing to sip from a glass of whisky with considerable difficulty.

I ride Troy to give him exercise when there is no work to do on the land, but he had not been ridden much, and is not well schooled. He sometimes behaves like a four-year-old stallion, frisking around, nostrils flaring. If there is something that frightens him, he does a war dance on the spot, and refuses to move until he has been reassured like a baby that there is nothing there but a leaf or a shadow. Sometimes we go up the hill to the common, where you can see for miles, and there is never a soul to be seen – but Troy sees a bogey man in every bush!

Once when I was riding him, I noticed a strange rhythm to the sound of his hoofs on the road. When I asked him to trot, he obliged, but his head poked down, and he was clearly unbalanced. I turned around and came home. When I led him out to pasture he was holding his near hind leg strangely.

The next morning it was no better, and I called the vet. After initial tests, the removal of his shoes, and finally X-rays, no definite cause could be found. Troy continued to get worse, and was hanging his leg badly. I telephoned George Smith to see if Troy had ever had a similar problem. He hadn't, but George suggested calling in an osteopath. I finally found an veterinary osteopath in Gloucester. She was a small, slightly built young woman, and I couldn't help thinking as I looked at her that she would have a job doing any kind of manipulation on a big animal like Troy. She was equipped with a stool, on which she had to stand in order to examine Troy. Her diagnosis was that he had dislocated his pelvis. I have to admit that I was sceptical. She then mounted her stool, standing directly behind Troy, and proceeded to carry out some almost invisible movements, culminating in a sudden jerk. Troy leaped sideways, and she hastily removed herself and her stool from behind him.

"Lead him out of the stable," she commanded.

Troy walked out of the stable as if there had never been anything wrong with him.

In the summer of 1995 we had a garden party, and invited all our friends and neighbours. I was standing on the porch next to Brian Morgan and Aubrey Jones (my cousin Sally's father-in-law), and we were looking at Troy, who was standing watching us at the paddock fence.

Suddenly a piping voice called out, "Oh look! He's got his didgeridoo out!"

It was Sally, who, as a horse owner obviously felt

no embarrassment in pointing out one of Troy's larger attributes. However, I had found that farmers don't talk openly about such matters, so I hastily interjected, "It's because he's happy!" Quick as a flash came a mutter from Aubrey; Brian Morgan was convulsed with mirth. "What did he say?" I asked him.

Through his laughter, Brian replied, "He says he hasn't been happy for a long time!"

We have had to learn a whole new language concerning animals and their reproductive habits. Sheep, of different genders and at different stages, can be rams, tups, wethers, ewes, lambs, hoggetts, shearlings, gimmers, or theaves, and a female sheep is tupped. Cattle can be heifers, cows, bulls, bullocks or steers, and a cow is served. Pigs are gilts, sows, hogs, boars, weaners, porkers, cutters or baconers, and a sow is covered. Hens are trodden, and geese actually mate!

The animal who is now responsible for the siring of all our piglets is an amazing and wonderful Tamworth boar called Thomas (intimately known as John). We had used another boar, Basil, since Billy's contribution, who came from Cotswold Farm Park, but now that we had enough sows and gilts of our own for breeding purposes, we were free to use our own boar in future. This would save the constant search for a suitable boar, and all the work that this entails, but we had to find a pedigree Tamworth boar who was unrelated, and young enough to be able to serve our two gilts, Tinkerbell and Tulip, daughters of Tallulah and Tess. We found Tommy at Her Majesty's Prison, Hewell Grange, in Redditch. Hewell Grange Dreamboy 435, TW/1/HMR/435/95 was the brother of the boar who had been selected as best boar at the Royal Welsh Show that summer. He was then seven months old, and almost ready to start work.

We went to Hewell Grange Prison to collect him. We swept into the forecourt of the imposing building, with the trailer clattering along behind us. There was no one about, and I made my way to the huge door in the front. I felt a little out of place in my muddy farm clothes, as I was immediately surrounded by immaculately dressed prison guards. They were extremely polite and helpful – we had come to the wrong entrance. The farm manager was at lunch, but we could wait in the waiting room and have a cup of coffee. We had the dogs with us in the car, so we decided to drive over to the farm and have a look around.

The farm looked very tidy and well run, lots of free-range Tamworth pigs, and some sleek-looking rare breed cattle. A group of men soon arrived back from their lunch break. They were very chatty, and showed us where our young boar was penned up ready for us. It transpired that these were prisoners who did the labour on the farm. Tommy looked a fine little boar, and when the farm manager arrived we clinched the deal without more ado.

When we arrived home, Tommy trotted out of the trailer with alacrity and was introduced to Tess, who was already in pig. He seemed very pleased with his new lady friend and soon made himself at home.

The gilts were still a little young for Tommy's attentions, and we arranged that he was to go 'on the road' when we brought Tess in to farrow. His first date was with a Tamworth gilt called Daisy, who lived not far away. He stayed with Daisy for three weeks, and in due course she had eight piglets. Soon after that, we had an extremely nice Tamworth sow to visit us here for three weeks. She was a pet pig who had the run of the farm when she was at home, and Tommy has since been to stay at her place, where he has a fine old time, and seemed very pleased to see his progeny from their last meeting, who were still very much on the scene.

At one of the farms he visited, Tommy and his sow were loose in a courtyard adjoining the farmhouse, and he soon sussed out that there was a warm kitchen just inside the back door. The lady of the house came in to find Tommy stretched out in front of the Aga, very much at home. It appears that she hadn't the heart to exert her authority, and, for the rest of his stay, Tommy divided his attentions between the sow and the Aga!

After these excursions Tommy came home to serve the gilts, and then Tess a few months later. Tess still had some of her piglets with her, and although they were officially weaned, they liked to suckle Mum in the morning before their breakfast arrived. One foggy day, Roger was approaching the field with the pig food, when he saw what looked like a small mountain looming out of the mist. As he got nearer he made out the shapes of Tess, standing still, with six large piglets suckling her from both sides, and Tommy firmly astride the mountain, looking extremely pleased with himself.

He has now served two other sows in the area, both Gloucester Old Spots, and also Sally and John Jones' two Sandy and Black sows – twice. All his concubines have produced large litters, and Tess's last litter was twelve. The two smallest piglets were soon relegated to the back teats, which were not producing enough milk. They were not making much progress, so we acquired some sow-milk replacer and started to bottle feed them. They screamed loudly when they were picked up, and fought vigorously against the rubber lambs' teat, which they had difficulty sucking, so we bought some human baby bottles and teats. This was much more successful, and although still a bit of a struggle initially, they soon ran to be picked up and fed – even leaving Mum if she had the bar open! We bottle fed three times a day, then twice, and finally once (although it was no longer necessary) so that Touch Productions could film them running across the field for their treat. Unfortunately, they were so excited by all the activity that they didn't perform, and when they eventually got hold of the teat, one of them swallowed it! That was definitely the last time we bottle fed them. When we sold the litter, it was impossible to distinguish the two runts, and one was actually chosen for breeding. To date Tommy has fathered 106 piglets, and he is not yet two years old!

By now we had also acquired an Indian Game cock and hen, a Speckled Sussex hen, a Silver Dorking, and in addition, as an indulgence for me, a little Millefleur and two Silkie hens for the courtyard. The larger birds were to be kept free-range in the fields, to multiply, give us eggs, and in due course, meat. The Silkies were to adorn the courtyard and to hatch extra eggs for us when they went broody. Molly, the Millefleur, was there to look beautiful (but she lays a little egg every day).

All this was going according to plan, but as the field hens grew larger they started to fly over their electric netting. The Silver Dorking got into the wood and was killed by a fox. We have since replaced her, but we were upset, and determined not to let it happen again. We were told that Aubrey Jones was an expert wing clipper, and he duly arrived with a large pair of scissors to do the job for us. I caught the birds one by one (I don't think Aubrey was too keen on handling the Indian Game cock, who has long, thick legs with inch-long spurs), and Aubrey confidently cut a section of wing feathers from each bird. We thanked him profusely, and waved him goodbye. Aubrey had barely driven round the corner when we saw two of the hens he had clipped fly over the netting! I rushed to my books to see what could be done – Aubrey had cut the wrong feathers! Well, it was a long time since he'd last done it, and he gave me the courage to have a go myself. It's a bit daunting the first time you cut through those big feathers, so close to the quill blood vessels. I felt very proud when it worked, and it's now a regular task as the feathers grow.

Cecil, the Silkie cock, started life as a hen. I don't

know if the change of sex unbalanced him, but he began to get quite fierce. The Indian Game cock, is a force to be reckoned with, but he is not normally aggressive. Cecil, on the other hand, would run up people's legs and attack them. He started with the hapless builders, who were by now terrified of entering the courtyard, and then started on my daughter, and worst of all, her little son Florek. After this he tried it on me, and I had to arm myself with a stick when I was working in the courtyard. We knew that we must do something about Cecil before my little grandson came to visit again, but he was a beautiful bird, and one of our first group of hens, so we were putting off the dreadful day. In the end, fate took a hand. One of Cecil's young sons decided it was time he was cock o' the roost, and he started a fight. When we came upon them, Cecil was very much the worse for wear, and would probably have gone on to a painful death. We grabbed him, and shut him in the hen house.

But alas, Cecil's time had come, and he was the first bird that Roger had had to slaughter. Although he has killed more than a dozen hens now, he's still apprehensive when the time comes. Originally this was because he feared that he might not kill the bird cleanly, and it would suffer unnecessarily, but this has never been the case. He's now confident of his technique: the bird is dead within a fraction of a second, although the body movements go on for some minutes. I think we both hate it because it seems so unfair. One day, the hen is clucking around with its mates, eating the wheat grain scattered on the field and tucked up safely from foxes in its hen house at night, and the next, a superior human being comes along and ends it all by breaking its neck. What right have we to do that?

I fed the hens in the evening, and in the early days, when we had only two pigs, I used to do the evening round, cleaning the outhouses, feeding the animals and tucking them up for the night. I did the round in the same order every night, starting with the hens: calling them by name, I would lead them up to the hen house, feed them, and shut them in. The pigs were next, then Jonnie and the sheep. I had a companion on my rounds, a little black cat called Mouse. Mouse and her brother Rat were two fierce little kittens given to me by Sally to live in the barn and catch rodents. They had been born in Sally's stable, and it took her two days to catch them. She arrived with them in a cat basket, wearing thick leather gloves. The noise from the basket sounded like lion cubs. After we had released them into the barn we didn't see them for several weeks, although the food and milk we put down for them was disappearing. Gradually we caught glimpses of them as they came for their food, and in due course were able to touch them. Mouse eventually became very tame, but Rat was always wary. Mouse soon learned the order of the evening round, and just before I moved on to the next section, she would race ahead and sit waiting for my arrival. She had no fear of any of the animals, and would go in with the pigs and the cow, and liked to sleep in the cow shed with Jonnie and watch the milking in the morning. Her mating was out of our control, and she had several admirers; tom cats who would come to pay suit, stay for a few days, and then move on. Her two main suitors we christened Stoat and Vole, but whether one of them was the father of her kittens, or whether it was incest, we are not sure. Her first batch of kittens did not survive, and we never saw them, but she had a second litter, two tabby cats and one black, which she proudly led out of the hay bales to show us when they were about eight weeks old. As she herself was a very small cat, we thought that we now had a big enough complement of barn cats, and had her neutered. We couldn't catch Rat to get him neutered – he had become a wanderer, although he still came and went.

The day Mouse was due to have her stitches out, she came up to me when I was working in the vegetable garden, stretched up against me and asked to be picked up. I gave her a kiss and told her that I would come and take her stitches out when I had finished gardening. We never saw her again. Days later, after we had searched and telephoned, I recalled how one of my cats in London had behaved in a similar manner, stretching up and asking to be picked up when I was giving him breakfast. He was run over later that morning. They say that cats have a sixth sense.

The kittens were now eating well, and they soon became very friendly. I'm afraid I spoiled them, and used to feed them at the back door. Winter approached, and as we sat snugly in the sitting room in the evening, three little faces used to appear at the window. They would sit and watch us for a long time, mewing forlornly if we looked at them. One snowy night, I could bear it no longer, and much against Roger's wishes, I brought them in. Mole, Ratkin and Mousel. What delight.

"They'll come in anyway, in the summer," I said.

Sadly, Mousel also disappeared a few months later. We had Ratkin neutered so that he wouldn't wander, but Mole was to be the mother of a new generation of barn cats, and she duly got pregnant and had her kittens in the barn: Mouse Too, Weasel, and Rabbit. I was very severe with myself this time, and deliberately didn't get too friendly with them, and they have remained barn cats; although they look through the window at times, they don't try to come in. They are very good friends with Płatek, particularly Mouse Too who rubs himself against him when they meet in the barn. Mole and Ratkin also love Płatek, and greet him when they meet with rolls, head rubbing, and by walking on their hind legs. Xanadu is inclined to snap at them and doesn't get the same treatment.

We thought we now had enough cats, but Mole got pregnant again before we had taken action. This time she had her kittens in the stable, but when they were only a few weeks old, she carried them in through the cat flap, one by one. Roger pretended to be horrified, but it was obvious that he was as pleased as I was! I made up a bed for them in a corner, and then went to make sure there were none left behind. There was a loud mewing coming from behind the manger, and sure enough there was one little kitten left behind. He looked very small and weak, although he was crying loudly. I brought him in, but he grew rapidly weaker, and died two days later. I think Mole had abandoned him deliberately. The remaining three kittens we called Butler (because he was black with white spats and vest), Tiger, and Bajers (he had beige ears!). We became totally besotted with the three little newcomers, who had inherited their mother's gentle and playful nature, but we already had seven cats, including the barn cats, and it would have been madness to keep them. Their antics were entrancing, especially when they patted Płatek on the nose with their sharp little claws, and the day that they were to go to new homes was a sad one for us. The house felt strangely empty for a long time, but we were delighted to have news of them all from Vivien Coombe of the Cats' Protection League, who had found them homes: she said that two were together and were great friends with the family puppy, and the other (Bajers, the boldest one) had made friends with the family cat and was "very funny, brave as a lion, a real hooligan!"

My other two house cats were delighted to see the departure of the kittens. We still had Zari, the shy one, but our dear Zala had died at the age of twelve. We had him with us for another two years after he had been lost, but he became ill with cancer, and we had no choice but to have him put to sleep. Zala had had difficulty breathing all weekend, and had stayed in the bedroom, scarcely moving. The vet had advised us that we must decide when he was in too much pain to continue. I was afraid he would go out and would be too weak to return, and we wouldn't know where he was, or if he was alive – which had been the case when he was lost two years before.

We called the vet on Monday morning. It was a sunny day and Zala got up for the first time in a couple of days, and came downstairs. He sat in a patch of sunlight on the kitchen floor washing himself, and then managed to jump up to the ledge where the cat food was and he ate a little fish. Just then the vet arrived. She had come to put Zala out of his pain, but now I didn't know what to do. She didn't press us, but when she had examined Zala's frail body, she said that she thought he was near death, and that to prolong his life would probably prolong his suffering. I held him in my arms while she prepared to inject his thin little leg, but he seemed to realise what was happening and began to struggle violently. I don't know where he found the strength from. The tears were streaming down my face.

She asked, "Shall I go on?" I nodded.

He fought to the last. I felt like a murderer.

Even now I say to Roger, "Did I do the right thing, taking his life?"

"Yes, it had to be done, his pain would have become unbearable."

I try not to have favourites, but Zala was a very, very special cat. We buried him under a rose tree in the garden.

Zala and Zari were Russian Blues, definitely town cats, and after Zala's death Zari seemed as miserable as we were. Heather and Walter's daughter had two kittens she was giving away, and we were sorely tempted to take them both, but we chose a little ginger ball of fluff whom we called Newport and he's a real character. So now the house contingent consists of Zari, Newport, Mole and Ratkin, and the barn population of Weasel, Rabbit and Mouse Too. We had Mole neutered, although we nearly weakened and let her have 'just one more litter!'

We have to buy the food for the cats and the dogs, but until now we had also bought in all the meal for the pigs and it was proving a major expense – it was time we learned how to be self-sufficient. Even grassland has to be managed. We had to find out what seed to plant, if and when it should be cut, when to put the stock to graze on it, and when to cut it for hay. In the winter, when grass was in short supply, we had to have other crops to supplement the grass. What should we choose? What would grow best at an altitude of 200 metres? When should it be planted and when harvested? How should it be stored? How long would it store for? Roger undertook the task of working out a rotation.

From the outset Roger had wanted to be self-sufficient, but to be 100 per cent self-sufficient would require too many sacrifices: we would have to give up champagne, and olive oil, and bananas, and fuel for the central heating – though we did investigate hot water fuelled by the compost heap! So the goal was to be financially self-sufficient, using the sale of surplus produce to buy the things we couldn't produce ourselves. Broadly speaking, this meant producing all the meat and vegetables and most of the fruit for our own consumption, and all the food for the stock. There are usually only the two of us to feed, but we have visits from friends and relations on a regular basis, so we planned on feeding four adults.

We had no idea how much land this would necessitate, but we had thought that 5 hectares would be enough, and it was really all we could afford when we bought Upper Bridge Court. Now we wish we had more, but it would be pointless trying to buy it back, or to buy a field or two from our neighbouring farmers, because their answers would be pretty short!

Despite the fact that acres are a part of our traditional heritage, which Roger holds very dear, he says he can estimate a hectare of land more easily than an acre. A hectare is 100 metres by 100 metres (approximately 100 by 100 paces), and is easier to envisage than an acre, which is 4,840 square yards.

When we moved in, David Griffiths, who had been tenanted to the land for years, had a grass ley down in one field, had recently harvested barley from the other, and had grazed sheep in the paddock. Because we had so much work to do on the house, we arranged that David could continue to use our two fields until the following summer. That October, he sowed barley again in the south field, for harvesting the following August, and put his sheep to over-winter on the grass ley in the east field. In the spring he let the grass grow, and cut it for silage (a method of preserving forage crops while still moist and succulent) in June. By this time we already had geese, pigs, a cow and sheep, so David vacated the land after he had taken his crops.

By now, Roger knew a lot more about how much land we needed, and what factors should be taken into account, such as the altitude, the climate, and the fertility. We wanted to build the soil fertility in a natural, organic way, rather than putting chemicals on the land. The natural way was to use the stock to manure the soil, and to rotate the crops. Chemical fertilisers make the crops very lush, but more prone to disease and attack by aphids and birds, and they also affect the soil structure. Each crop gives and takes different things from the soil, and, with careful planning in an organic system, the soil fertility can be built rather than depleted. Furthermore, because the crops are rotated, the stock are rotated as well, fertilising different areas, and having regular clean grazing. This prevents the parasites associated with any one breed from accumulating, and reduces the need for regular worming.

We're also very keen to encourage wild life on our farm, not just for the environment, but also to help our crops: many mammals and insects keep the pests that attack plants under control. For instance, ladybirds like nettles and eat thousands of aphids. So it's a good idea to keep nettles near your crops. To do this, we keep a margin of at least 2 metres of uncultivated land around our fields, which also act as wild life corridors.

When we lived in London, although we enjoyed

food, we didn't pay too much attention to where it came from or how it was produced. We ate a lot of fresh fruit and vegetables, not too much fat or sugar, we didn't eat veal because of veal crates, nor *pâté de fois gras* because of force-feeding geese but, beyond that, we didn't investigate.

As we learned about farming, we naturally became organic farmers. It seemed to us to be wrong to feed our animals growth promoters and prophylactic antibiotics and not to allow them enough space to lead a natural existence. It seemed to us to be wrong to pour chemicals on the land to increase our crop yields and kill weeds (and vital organisms in the soil as well). It seemed to us to be wrong to remove hedges and trees, and to plough the land up to a wire fence to create more space to grow crops or keep more livestock, and to deny corridors around our fields for wild life.

A good definition of organic farming has been provided by the UK Register of Organic Food Standards: "Organic production systems are designed to produce optimum quantities of food of high nutritional quality by using management practices which aim to avoid the use of agrochemical inputs and which minimise damage to the environment and wildlife." The principles include: working with natural systems rather than seeking to dominate them; the encouragement of biological cycles involving microorganisms, soil flora and fauna, plants and animals; and ensuring that all farm animals are carefree, healthy and happy whilst minimising the need for chemical medication.

But, we're lucky. We can afford to be organic. We don't have to depend on farming to provide us with a basic living. Farming needs a lot of capital investment in land, buildings and equipment, for a low return. A low return because food is too cheap. Economics drive the farmer to extract the maximum return out of his large capital investment, through intensive farming. And the Common Agricultural Policy (CAP), through its subsidies based on the number of animals or the tons of produce, encourages the farmer to be more intensive.

But can anybody afford not to buy organic food or farm organically? Nature has already taken her revenge with the tragedy of BSE and its probable link with CJD. Are there any other links between intensive farming and human disease? Many carrots are sprayed with toxic organophosphate insecticides to control the carrot root fly. In the past, this has led to some carrots having unexpectedly high residues of organophosphate insecticides. One of the government recommendations was to top and tail and peel carrots to remove traces of the chemical before eating it. In the organic system we don't use any chemicals on any produce – so we have no necessity to peel our carrots, thereby preserving most of the nutrients which are in the skin – and, incidentally, we think they taste incomparably better. And what about Genetically Modified Organisms (GMOs)? Recently, the Consumers' Association's magazine *Which?* has pointed out that prophylactic antibiotics and antibiotics as growth promoters in farm animals are getting into the food chain and could reduce, thereby, the effectiveness of antibiotics in humans. GMOs use antibiotics as a marker gene, so any GMO product has a trace of antibiotic in it which, once in the body, could reduce the effectiveness of antibiotics by this route also. There are umpteen other examples.

One opinion is that science will keep ahead of BSE and the GMO problems and keep our food safe. Our view is that Nature, not man, will triumph in the end. So we should all now think more carefully about what we eat, and the processes and the suffering it has gone through to get onto our plate.

Such a change is going to take years, but we can focus on a few vital actions now. Firstly, the consumer must demand that the food he buys is organic. Secondly, UKROF or MAFF should make sure the public understand that only organic food is labelled 'organic' since it is now illegal to use the word organic otherwise (and many foods are betwixt and between under a variety of promotional labels). Thirdly, the organic organisations and the supermarkets should join forces to advertise and publicise the benefits of organic produce. And finally, the CAP has to be overhauled, so that, instead of paying farmers to produce more food, they should be paid to protect our precious countryside. Perhaps this could be based in part on the miles of hedges or stone walls farmers plant or build and maintain on their land, which satellites can measure? This would also have the effect of giving more financial support to the smaller farmer, who operates on a small profit margin.

Financially, the consumer would pay more (but not much more if a significant amount of food was organic), the farmer would get more for his produce but less from the new CAP, and therefore the consumer would pay less for the CAP. But look at the benefits: good, wholesome, safe, nutritious food; happy, healthy, stress-free farm animals; and a countryside that our children's children can be proud of.

To put our principles into practice, we needed regular and expert advice, and we joined the Organic Advisory Service at Elm Farm Research Centre in Berkshire. Mark Measures came to the farm, and from that meeting evolved the rotation we have now used for over two years.

The rotation that Mark Measures designed was based on six stages, by dividing each of the two fields into three strips of equal areas. Three strips would be grass; one wheat; one swedes with fodder peas; and one barley with oats. Each year the crops would rotate anticlockwise and be planted on the next adjacent strip. Because three adjacent stages were grass, each grass strip would remain planted for three years, but all the other crops would be replanted each year.

About every six months the animals are moved to another strip for clean grazing. The cattle and the sheep share the same strip, but the grazing is rationed by moving the electric fence, step by step, across the strip every two months. The hens also share this strip, and have an electric netting enclosure (connected to the fence to energise it), not only to keep them in, but, more importantly, to keep Mr Reynard out. Troy pulls the hen house for us, and we move the hens every month to a new part of the enclosure. Since we have used this system, we haven't lost any more hens to foxes – unfortunately we lost three earlier.

The rotation creates a lot of work in itself. Every year, two-thirds of the land has to be ploughed, prepared, seeded and harvested. All the stock and their electric fences have to be moved two or three times a year, and the stock have to be parked somewhere meanwhile. On the positive side, all our produce will be organic (full organic registration is scheduled for January 1998) so, for example, a problem like BSE couldn't occur in our beef – as is the case for all beef produced on organic farms in the UK.

Electric fencing is one of the tools that makes a rotation like this possible. The fence has to be high quality to prevent the cattle and sheep trampling on the wheat or, much worse, the pigs routing it up! We have two separate fences running all the time and they run on 12-volt leisure batteries, the same type that are used in caravans and boats. They must be kept fully charged, and it's a weekly chore to carry a newly charged battery several hundred yards to replace the one that's gone flat. Roger checks the fences with a test meter every time he feeds the stock, and, if the voltage is too low and the problem is not the battery, he walks the perimeter of the fence looking for the problem. This could be, in the case of the pigs, an offending clod of earth which they have routed onto the wire. In the summer the grass can grow up and earth the bottom wire, so it has to be strimmed under the full length of the fences (normally about half a mile). But the biggest problem is snow – not the dry, powdery sort but the wet, clinging sort. It sticks to the wires and they sag to the ground, earthing themselves. The only solution is to remove the snow by walking round the fence, running the wire between your fingers. If the snow is deep enough to cover the bottom wire, the current to that wire can be disconnected. We're planning to change to fences driven by mains electricity rather than batteries, which will save time and provide a much more reliable electric fence.

One morning, as Roger was feeding the hens, he noticed Płatek sniffing the ground very close to the electric netting around the hen enclosure – unusual for him because he's petrified of it. On closer investigation he found a hedgehog who had tried to crawl through the netting but was too big for the hole in it. His spines had got caught and he could neither advance nor retreat; his little body was pulsating with electric shocks at one second intervals. Roger switched off the fence, freed the hedgehog, and placed him underneath the hedgerow. He didn't move, but his body continued to pulsate at the same rate. We looked for him later that day, but he was nowhere to be seen. If you ever find a pulsating hedgehog, you'll know where he's come from!

The fence normally gives an impulse of 8,000 volts

and new animals learn very quickly not to touch it. They get so conditioned, that, if the fence fails, they won't cross it – until they realise, after a few days, that it doesn't hurt any more. Tommy became so fearful of it that, once, when we were trying to move him, and opened the electric ribbons that form the gate, he wouldn't cross the invisible line. It took a bucketful of apples in front and lot of pushing from behind, before he plucked up enough courage and made a dash for it. Roger got too confident about stepping over it when feeding the animals, and received 8,000 volts where it hurts most!

The pigs, the sheep, the cattle and the horse learned very quickly and have never gone through the electric fence, except when the sheep had New Forest Eye disease and some were temporarily blind. All these animals move around a new area, exploring it carefully, and, once they have touched the wire a few times, they rarely touch it again. Small piglets, on the other hand, tend to rush around like maniacs and the first time they are introduced to an electric fence, they will burst through it, the electric shock accelerating them on their way. Consequently, a few days before they are due to move out of the pigsty to one of the fields, we train the piglets by setting up a small electric fence ring outside the sty (where they are born), but within our walled courtyard – then we let the family into this small ring. If they do shoot through it, they can't go far, and within a couple of hours they've developed a healthy respect for the wire.

Early one morning Roger was feeding the pigs in

the field, and the ritual was being filmed by Touch Productions. We had just moved the pigs to clean pasture, and had made two adjacent enclosures with the electric fencing. Tommy and Tess and Tess's piglets were on one side, and Tinkerbell and Tulip (with whom Tommy was not supposed to fraternise), together with their piglets, were on the other. Roger had just fed Tommy and Tess, and had stepped over the fence to feed the others. As he was finishing, he realised that there were *three* large pigs with their heads in the trough amongst the piglets.

The film crew were creased up with laughter, "Tommy jumped over the fence."

This was at eight o'clock in the morning, and I was hastily summoned on the field telephone to help get Tommy back into his own quarters in case he turned his attentions to the young sows. Fortunately he only seemed interested in the food, which perhaps bears out Maslow's hierarchy of needs – at least in its application to pigs!

We tried lifting the fence and encouraging Tommy to walk under it with a bucket of food under his nose, but he had by now remembered that an electric fence hurts. Perhaps he had brushed the fence 'with the inside of his thigh' as he jumped over it (as Brian Johnson once famously said of Ian Botham when he knocked one of his bails off). In the end, we had to back the trailer into the enclosure, load Tommy into it, keeping all the piglets and the sows at bay, drive the trailer into the other enclosure, and unload him again. If only Touch Productions could be there with their cameras when everything is going well!

We tamed the Hebrideans with soft words and titbits

Bramble's lamb, Buzz, with her own twin lambs, at birth

Emral Constellation (Jonquil) joins the family

Josh's arrival

Roger milking, with a little help from Josh

Jonnie, Josh, Roger and Płatek

Troy being shod

Meriel and Troy collecting stones

Meriel riding Troy on the common, with the dogs

Roger and Troy harrowing

POT OF GOLD

Our Tommy, not yet two years old ...

... and some of his 106 progeny

Tinkerbell, Tulip and their piglets, in their wallow

Brian and Richard shearing in the barn

Part of the crop rotation

Tacking Troy to the cart

Since then we've raised the height of the top wire considerably – it used to be set as per the manufacturer's recommendations, but obviously they hadn't reckoned on Tommy!

Moving the pigs creates quite a challenge. The theory is simple. First move them out of their electric fence enclosure to a temporary parking place (usually the wood), dismantle and then reinstall the electric fence in a new area, and finally move the pigs from the wood to the new enclosure – this might involve getting the pigs into the trailer. The sows and boar are not too difficult: I go in front with a bucket of food, and Roger brings up the rear with a couple of pig boards or hurdles to try to keep them all together. Piglets, on the other hand, are not so co-operative.

On one occasion, Roger decided to try to move our sow, Tess, and her six piglets to the wood by himself, while I was out. This was Tess's second litter, so she was now a mature sow of about 200 kilos; the piglets were three or four months old, and weighed between 30 and 40 kilos each. The wood was 200 metres away from the pigs' present home, with the electric fence running parallel all the way to it, creating a corridor about three metres wide, along which we could drive the pigs when the time came to move them. Roger opened the gate leading from the pigs' enclosure into the corridor and put some food on the ground. The herd came out to eat the food, and Roger followed, carrying two 6-foot hurdles that he'd tied together to make a large V, blocking their retreat and pushing them along the corridor to the wood.

Tess trotted along the corridor in the right direction and the piglets duly followed. All was going well, until, when he was about half-way along, one of the piglets decided he'd like to return to what had been his home for most of his life. He turned around and rammed the hurdles, easily lifting them up with his snout and hightailing it back home. Roger thought he'd better continue driving the rest of the herd to the wood (which he managed successfully), and then turn his attention to the one that had got away.

An hour later an exhausted Roger was still trying to catch the piglet in the field. The pig enclosure was a rectangle of about 3,000 square metres, and there was nowhere to corner the little boar. He didn't remember that Tess and his siblings had gone along the corridor, so he walked around the perimeter crying for his mummy. If Roger approached him, he raced off at high speed, and evaded all attempts to trap him with the hurdles. Eventually it started to rain. Pigs don't like the rain, and the boarlet beetled into the pig ark in the middle of the enclosure.

The ark is made of wood with two curved sheets of corrugated steel giving it a semicircular elevation 4 feet in height. The front and back are covered with inch-thick block board, with a hole cut to form a doorway big enough for an adult pig. Roger slowly tiptoed towards the ark until he was standing beside the doorway, and, taking a deep breath, flung himself into the ark entrance, blocking the doorway completely.

All hell broke loose. The piglet careered around in the confined space, straw flying everywhere, until he realised he was trapped. Then he stood at the far end of the ark, his small eyes watching wildly. Now Roger had to grab him without un-blocking the doorway. Extending his arms to double their length, he somehow managed to grab a leg without opening the escape route. Pigs are very strong animals and they wriggle and squirm with all their might when captured. We have found that the best way to carry them is to wrap your arms around their tummy, allowing their legs to kick freely. After a long battle, carried out from a kneeling position (the roof of the ark is only four feet in the middle), Roger managed to get his arms around the boarlet, and, clasping him to his chest, started shuffling to the doorway on his knees. Unfortunately, he couldn't get through the doorway in this position, so, holding the piglet's front legs as tightly possible, he put him down and clambered out backwards, dragging the poor piglet in front of him. By now, Roger was completely exhausted, but he still had to get to the wood, and, if he let go now, he would be back to square one. He managed to get his arms firmly around the struggling piglet once more and heave all 35 kilos off the ground. Now he had to carry the writhing, screaming, ginger rubber ball the 200 metres to the wood. Somehow he made it, and, with one last heave, lifted him over the 4-foot-high fence and lowered him to the ground.

Here I found him, collapsed in a heap.

"There must be an easier way of taking early retirement," he gasped.

Moving the animals can cause complications, but there are other problems in running a farm organically, and one of them is weeds – especially docks. When we started to use the land in 1994, Richard, through a misunderstanding, ploughed up a strip in the autumn rather than the following spring. After a lot of discussion, we decided to leave it fallow over the winter. Docks don't like competition from other plants, and this strip was bare. By March the docks were sprouting thickly. Docks have a tap root which can grow to a couple of feet in length, and Roger started digging them out by hand, thinking it would take him a couple of weeks. It took him three months as he methodically worked over nearly 4,000 square metres. He had some very welcome help from visitors, but as fast as he dug, more of the damn things sprouted up behind him. Consequently, the fodder peas were sown very late and a poor crop resulted.

The pigs will root out docks when the ground is soft, mainly because of the winter rain, but they won't eat them, so it has become a routine job, usually combined with feeding the stock, to walk around the pig area and collect the dock roots on the surface. This takes a long time because Tommy, the boar, gives you hefty pushes to ask for his regular cuddles and, as he weighs about 250 kilos, and sports two small, sharp tusks, one tends to oblige.

On the advice of Mark Measures, we also tried rotavating a strip before the wheat was sown in 1995 to try to suppress the docks. This was the only time that Richard and Brian criticised our methods – they told us, after they had stopped laughing, that we must be mad. The rotavator shreds the ground down to an adjustable depth of several inches. Mark had recommended three or four inches, so that the crowns and the tops of the docks would be cut off, on the theory that this is the fertile bit. The Morgans' experience was that it had chopped up docks and produced a bigger problem. Despite these warnings (re-enforced by Lee), Brian went ahead and rotavated it for us. We then spent two or three weeks harrowing the strip time and again with Troy, and picking up by hand the dock roots that this brought to the surface. There is no doubt that there were a lot less docks in the wheat crop the following summer!

Finally, it is essential that, as well as trying to eradicate docks by removing the roots, no seed must be allowed to get back into the system, either by falling on the ground to sprout a new plant, or by getting into the animal feed, and, through their guts, back to the ground in the manure. So each summer we cut every dock flower on the whole farm from the hedgerows, the field margins, and from within the crops. They then have to be collected and burnt.

So, with Brian's rotavating, the pigs routing, Troy's harrowing and a lot of hard work, I think we are winning the battle of the docks. Of course, we will never eradicate them. Every dock plant has hundreds of seeds and they can lie dormant in the ground for years before they decide to sprout.

The Harvest

In festive silks, purple, cerise and gold,
The people scramble upwards, breast to breast
With the great mountain. In his fiery hold
Is every islander who had transgressed
His laws of life – his was the red wrath flung
Till boiling lava lapped their naked feet.
Trembling they climb to that gashed mouth –
  Agung –
With sacrifice of all they hold most sweet:
Young bull, warm nostrils flaring, muscled with
  life,
A creaking cart of offerings, the little goat,
And red-combed cockerel. Soon the flashing knife
Will offer up this pride, that tender throat.
Secret, aloof, within its bamboo crate,
A royal cat, grooming its fur, rides to its fate.

Joyce Brooke

The previous poem was written by my mother. She wrote poetry all her life, and after her death I collected the poems and had them published. This was my favourite, it touched a chord in me: the islanders trying to appease their gods with the sacrifice of their precious animals; the animals oblivious of their fate, dependent on their human owners.

Farm animals are dependent on us. It is the farmers' responsibility to treat them well, and our own personal objective to make their lives as happy as possible. Yet, however much we love them, if they are to survive, in the end, we must sacrifice them. We try to ensure that it is done as humanely as possible, so that, like the royal cat of Agung, their awareness is only of life.

We have to accept that if rare breeds are to survive they must be made to contribute commercially to their own survival. I find it difficult to have patience with those who say, "Oh! how can you kill these lovely creatures? How can you eat them?" Where does the meat come from that they eat? What were those neat packages in the supermarket beforehand? I prefer to eat an animal that I know has lived a free and happy life, and has been given no unnatural additives. Of course, we could become vegetarians, but the problem won't be solved until the whole world becomes vegetarian. So we can play our part by raising our animals in the most natural way, and ensuring that they are then slaughtered without pain, and with the least possible stress. At least, then, for every hen we kill, there could be one less that has to live in a cage for eight, short miserable weeks whilst it is overfed with growth promoters, its underdeveloped bones sometimes unable to withstand its rapid growth. For every litter of piglets we kill, there could be one less sow languishing in a farrowing crate. For every Joshua we kill, there could be one less calf that has to suffer in a truck for hours, or days, until it meets an unknown fate in the far corners of Europe.

This line of reasoning enables us to justify killing the animals we have so lovingly reared. But the apprehension, when the moment comes to kill, will never go away.

The animals are a part of our harvest. In the country, the harvest festival has more meaning. We still carry offerings to our God, but here we carry fruit and vegetables to church as tokens of thanksgiving for the fruits of harvest.

Our first harvest festival service in the village church was also the first time I met Aubrey. After the service, everyone reassembled in the church hall, and Aubrey stepped into the role he is frequently called upon to play – auctioneer. He makes an impressive job of it: woe betide the man or woman who tries to escape without a purchase!

The harvest is the pinnacle of the farming year. We get enormous satisfaction from seeing our crops being cut down, gathered up, and stored. We have three distinct groups of crops at Upper Bridge Court: the swedes; the hay and the fodder peas; and the corn – the barley, oats and wheat. Each crop is harvested differently.

But of course, before they are harvested, the crops have to be sown. Fodder peas and spring barley are sown in April, swedes in June, grass leys at the end of August, winter oats in September, and wheat in October.

When we took over the fields in the summer of 1994, the first job to be done to start the rotation going was to plough up the barley stubble and put a new grass ley on the whole field, forming the three grass strips of our six-stage rotation. This would probably be the biggest job we would ever do because, subsequently, we would work on only one strip at a time.

Richard and Brian did this job for us. We were surprised at the amount of work involved. They went over the whole 2 hectares nine times with a variety of implements: first for ploughing; then harrowing; then rolling and harrowing several times until they were satisfied with the tilth; and lastly they scattered the seed, before giving the land a final roll.

To set up the remaining three strips in the rotation as quickly as possible, over the next two years, winter wheat, fodder peas with swedes, and winter oats with spring barley were planted in the other field. When the spring barley was sown in the spring of 1996, all the field crops had been planted at least once and the rotation was in full operation.

Every year, all the crops are replanted on the adjacent strip, one new grass strip is sown, and the oldest (three-year-old) grass strip is ploughed up.

The three grass strips are sown with a rich mixture of grasses, herbs and clover, which replace some of the nutrients taken out of the land by the preceding crops. The grass is grazed by our cattle, sheep and hens and provides the hay for them to eat over the winter months. We move them to half a new strip every six months so their parasites left on the land die long before they graze that same piece of land again. Also, the move in April is timed to coincide with lambing, so that the lambs are born on clean (parasite-free) pasture.

Wheat is sown when the three-year-old grass ley is ploughed up. We graze the pigs on this ley between cutting the hay in June and sowing the wheat in October. We would like the pigs to plough up the ground for us, but in summer the ground is normally too hard for them to get their noses into it. It therefore has to be ploughed, then rolled and harrowed until the soil is of the right tilth to drill the seed into the ground. Ploughing takes two horses, and drilling seed can take three, as well as special horse-drawn equipment. Troy could do the harrowing, but because Brian and Richard are here with tractors ploughing and drilling, they also do the harrowing and rolling, and finish the job in a day or two.

So far, we've used an old wheat grain called Maris Widgeon. We bought six bags of grain in the first place, which produces two or three tons. We keep enough to sow the next year – and so on in perpetuity. Maris Widgeon is a very good wheat for bread, and the straw, being very long, is very good for thatching, but needs harvesting with an old threshing machine so that the straw is not chopped up. Just once, we would love to do it that way sometime.

Once the wheat is harvested in August, this strip of land is not used for crops until the following April.

Rather than leave the ground with just the wheat stubble on it and risk docks re-establishing themselves, we sow it with what's called a cover crop. We've tried mustard and more recently rye grass. This is something we are glad to do ourselves. Troy pulls the spike harrows over the stubble to break the soil up, then we use a seed fiddle to scatter the seed, and, finally, Troy chain harrows the strip to try to bury the seed below the surface. We then pray for rain.

The seed fiddle is an oblong box containing the seed, carried under your arm with a shoulder strap to take the weight. On the front is a horizontal disc as big as a saucer, with baffles along the radii onto which the seed dribbles. A spindle attached to the saucer has a thong around it, the ends of which are fixed to a stick about three feet long. The stick is horizontal and at right angles to the oblong box, and, as you walk up and down, you push and pull the stick (just like bowing a violin held under your arm), revolving the disc which scatters the seed.

It's important to walk up and down in parallel lines that are the correct distance apart, so that the seed thrown out from the fiddle covers the ground evenly. Last year, Roger forgot the formula and asked Lee to remind him.

"I'll come over and help," he said. "When do you want to do it?"

He came the next morning. Lee marked out the lines and Roger followed them, scattering the seed with the fiddle. They scattered the first half of the grain up and down, and the remaining half across the strip, to achieve a more even distribution. Over the next two or three hours they both walked miles. We were concerned about Lee, who had had a hip replacement operation only a couple of months earlier and the last thing we wanted was a bionic leg left to grow amongst the rye grass.

They were both very tired when they'd finished, but despite this, Lee suggested that they should tack up Troy to pull the chain harrows over the seed, as rain was forecast later in the day. Roger felt like pulling his boots off and sitting down with a beer, but Lee, in his gentle but firm way, persisted.

It took another half an hour to fetch Troy, tack him up, and take him back to the fields, collecting the chain harrows on the way. Meanwhile, the sky was becoming very black. Roger started to harrow, but Lee now had nothing to do.

"You're making a good job of that, Roger, I'll go home now and get my dinner," he said, as Troy swung Roger round a corner at the bottom of the field.

No sooner had Lee disappeared from view than it started to rain. Within a few minutes it was pouring. Roger was soon drenched, but he calculated that Lee couldn't have made it home and would also be soaked – this made him feel a little better as he slogged up and down in the rain. Troy was enjoying it. An hour and a half later they finished, both wet to the skin, and after another thirty minutes, with the tack in the cellar and Troy in his paddock with a cup of rolled oats in his belly, Roger was at last sitting down with his boots off and a beer in his hand – feeling very pleased with himself! Lee had been right as usual. The job was done, the seed had been well watered, and the rye grass had got off to a good start. (Lee wasn't soaked – he sheltered under a tree and got safely home for his dinner during a break in the storm.)

We have an important resident at Upper Bridge Court, who follows the sowing of the seed from strip to strip. His name is Jack Straw, and he is a very colourful scarecrow made by Lesley as a birthday present for Roger. The crows give him a wide berth, and familiarity has not bred contempt, even after two seasons.

It's important to sow the rye grass as soon as possible after the wheat harvest in August, because in October we have to put the pigs on half of this strip and we want as much grass as possible for them to graze. Because it is not yet well established, they soon graze it off, and as the ground is normally soft and wet at this time of year, they proceed to do the ploughing for us. The whole patch soon becomes a quagmire and feeding them becomes quite hazardous. Emptying the first bucket of feed into the trough is a dangerous moment, as a sow and seven piglets (with a combined weight of over 400 kilos) make a dash for the first morsel. Heaven help you if your legs are stuck in the mud between them and their food! Both of us have been brought down in the mud a few times, but once is too often.

In March, we move the pigs on to the second half of the strip (which now has a good covering of rye grass), and prepare the first half, that they have routed up, for sowing the fodder peas at the beginning of April. Troy pulls the spring tine harrows, which make a deep tilth and pull out any other dock

The Rotation

The six-year cycle for a typical strip in the six-strip rotation

All six strips follow the same cycle, each one a year later

The cattle, sheep and hens are moved to the new grass strip when the ewes start to lamb in April, so the lambs have clean grazing land

Each of the areas where the pigs graze is divided into three, one for each sow, so all newly born litters of piglets have clean grazing

Year	Month	Strip	
Year 1	**August**	New grass	
	April (lambing)	Hay	Grass *Cattle Sheep Hens*
Year 2	**October**	Grass for hay	
Year 3	**October**	Grass *Cattle Sheep Hens*	Grass
	April (lambing)	Grass for hay	
	June	Grass *Pigs*	
Year 4	**October**	Wheat	
	August	Rye grass	
Year 5	**October**	Rye grass *Pigs*	
	April	Peas	Rye grass *Pigs*
	June	Peas	Swedes
Year 6	**September**	Oats	Swedes
	April	Oats	Barley
	August		

roots which are just below the surface, to be picked up later by hand. Until now, we have asked Brian and Richard to drill the fodder peas. This places them within the soil, where they will germinate most easily, and are not exposed to the beaks of the crows. But next year, we will try sowing part of the strip ourselves: first harrowing it with the spring tines; then scattering the seed; and finally chain harrowing it with Troy. If this is successful, it will allow us to take on another of the cultivating tasks.

The same process is followed in June, when it is time to sow the swedes in the second half of the strip. The pigs have ploughed it, we've collected the dock roots, and Troy now harrows it with the spring tines. Because the swede seeds are tiny, it's possible to scatter them with the seed fiddle, followed by a final chain harrowing with Troy.

After the fodder peas are harvested in July, winter oats are sown in September, giving a couple of months to dig out any docks that have blossomed meanwhile. This is a job needing ploughing and drilling, so it is one that we will not be able to take over with one horse. Similarly, spring barley is sown in April after all the swedes have been dug up.

Once the barley and oats have been harvested the following August, this strip is put back to grass for three years, and the full rotational cycle has been completed.

We could say that the harvest begins with the swedes. We dig all the swedes out by hand over the winter months, from October until March. The digging becomes part of the feeding round, morning and evening. We dig up four bucketsful, two of which we give directly to the pigs (they can eat them whole, except for the very big swedes which we split in two), and two to the sheep and cattle. We have to pulp these, and we have an old pulping machine, rather like an overgrown Moulinex, that we work by hand. It pulps a bucketful in a couple of minutes if you're very fit. At the same time as we dig out the swedes, we dig out any weeds, particularly docks. For this reason, swedes and other root crops are known as cleaning crops, because it's possible to weed them, and thereby clean the ground, which you can't do so easily with fodder peas or corn. Swedes have a lot of foliage, which none of our livestock likes, so we cut it off and leave it on the ground as a green manure. It was amongst the rich swede foliage that we had our first pheasant shoot in October 1994.

We'd seen a lot of pheasants in the fields as we fed our stock, and decided to organise a small shoot. Richard, Brian and Walter arrived, suitably armed; Andrea and Mark (who were staying with us at the time), Roger and I, were delegated to act as beaters.

It was a cold autumn morning, bright and still. We stood in the garden around a large circular brass tray, and drank tiny glasses of sloe gin, made from our sloes, before setting forth to the fields in single file. The guns waited in the field, and the beaters climbed the fence into the wood and combed it to drive out any pheasants. We all then formed a long line in the field, and walked forwards slowly to flush any pheasants out of the undergrowth.

We'd almost cleared the swedes, and were approaching the next strip, which was bare at the time, when suddenly, and without any warning, a pheasant emerged at Andrea's feet and took off with its distinctive whirring of wings. All the novices started, especially Andrea, but Richard was calmly taking aim, and, when the pheasant was about 50 metres away, he fired and hit it. The pheasant fell to the ground and Brian ran to it and broke its neck immediately.

Having seen so many pheasants on the field in recent weeks, seeing only one all morning was a bit disappointing, but we'd had a new experience. The guns insisted we had the pheasant, and, on their advice, we hung it in the barn for three or four days. Roger plucked it very easily, but was horrified to find that it was thick with maggots around its vent. With some trepidation, he continued to dress it, and discovered that the maggots were only in the innards and not in the flesh – so we decided to eat it. It made an excellent meal!

In June, we harvest the first cut of hay from two of the grass strips. One of them has had no stock on it since April and the other since October. The Morgans cut it, tedder, or turn it a number of times to make sure it's dry, and then bale it. If it is baled wet, it rots very quickly, so it's vital to wait for a spell of fine weather to harvest the hay, or the crop (which is the basic food for the cattle, sheep and horse throughout the winter months) can be ruined.

Our first crop of hay in 1994 was taken in August, after David Griffiths had already taken a cut for silage in June. The late hay is called lattermath, or rowan, and is sometimes considered not as good as the first crop, either in quality or quantity, although many of the late-growing grasses are especially nutritious and, if cut when young, make the best hay of all. The shortening days and autumnal dews make the grass very succulent and more difficult to harvest as hay unless there is a spell of fine weather. We try to cut our hay early in June to catch the young crop, although the weather can also be unreliable at this time of year. We can then put the pigs to graze half the cut grass, and take lattermath from the other half in August. This makes sure that we have more than enough hay to see us through even the worst winter.

Initially, we used our Daihatsu Fourtrak and a flat-bed trailer to carry the hay bales to the barn. Since then, the weather has threatened, and we've resorted to mechanical means to get the hay into the barn as quickly as possible. But in a fine spell of weather we would use Troy, as we have done for the straw bales.

One Saturday during our first summer at Upper Bridge Court, when Lesley and Maciek were staying with us, we went out at about midnight, into the balmy night with the dogs, to stroll down the lanes. We saw lights in the fields on the Morgans' farm, and walked over to investigate. Brian and Richard were working into the night to get the hay bales under cover, because rain was forecast. They were getting tired, and Roger and Maciek offered to help. They all pulled together and got the rest of the bales off the field and into the barn. Now came the hardest part: stacking them more than 15 feet high. The last bales, weighing about 15 kilos each, have to be thrown to the top of the stack. It took another couple of hours, and I think Maciek and Roger were pretty sore the following day, but Richard and Brian said later that the additional help put new life into them when their spirits were flagging. It's good to be able to give a little help to those who give us so much.

We harvest the fodder peas in July, in the same way as hay, because this is the easiest method for us to gather and handle it. The idea is to keep the peas in the pods on the vine and bale it. The cattle, sheep and horse love it, although the cattle only digest the vine, not the peas. (Perhaps this means that we'll have nothing but peas growing here eventually, rather than docks!). It's critical to cut and bale the fodder peas at the right time. The first crop we had was not good: we harvested it too late, and most of the peas fell on the ground as we cut and baled it; the remaining vine was too dusty, and not very palatable – so we eventually made it into compost. The following year's crop, although it rained after it was cut and it had to lie on the ground for days to dry out, was much better, and was all eaten up.

The harvest with a capital H is the corn harvest in August. The key implement here is the combine harvester which Richard drives along the lanes to Upper Bridge Court. He and Brian have to take the front off the harvester and reassemble it here. The harvester cuts the corn, complete with its grain in the seed pod, takes it all in at the front, separates the grain (which it keeps in a hopper), and drops the straw out of the back ready to be baled. The grain is transferred to a trailer, which is then parked below the granary in the barn, and the grain is augered up into the granary. The auger is actually an auger inside a metal tube, turned by a motor, and the grain rides up it and out of the tube at the top. We recently had the granary repaired and created three bays in it, for barley, oats and wheat. Below the granary is the mill room, containing a roller mill and a grinder. Trap doors in the granary floor allow us to pour bucketfuls of grain into the mills.

The cattle, sheep and horse can eat rolled grain, simply squashed flat by passing the grain between two heavy rollers, but the grain must be ground for the pigs, so that they can digest it fully. Since the harvest of 1996 (our first full harvest of barley, oats and wheat), we have rolled all our own grain, but as the grinder is not working yet, we still have to buy all the feed for the pigs. Consequently, we have a lot of unused grain in the granary. Hopefully, we will get the grinder working well before the next harvest in August 1997 – or we won't have enough space for all the grain.

It was a wonderful moment when, having completed the harvest in 1996, our barn was bursting with the crops we had sown, nurtured and harvested. The bales of hay reached the underside of the stone-tiled roof as did the distinct stacks of barley, oat, and wheat straw and the bales of fodder peas. In the granary, the floor was bending under the 5 tons of barley, oat, and wheat grain in their separate hoppers.

Since October 1995, we've made all our own bread. We have a hand grinder to grind our wheat grain into flour. It's hard work, but it only takes a few minutes to grind a kilo for a couple of small loaves. We don't sieve out any of the husk, so it is truly wholemeal. Not having made bread before, it took a few weeks to get it right, and it's still a bit crumbly. A friend suggested cutting the loaves with an electric knife, which produced quite professional looking slices. We bake two small loaves twice a week, which takes about an hour, spread over a three hour period. It tastes delicious – newly baked with our own butter, it's a meal in itself.

Although the harvest marks the end of the farming year, it also marks the beginning of another. The process of regeneration is beginning again. Now the fields are ploughed and sown for the following year. Now the rams come in to service the ewes, so that the lambs will be born in the spring.

While we were building up our small flock of Hebridean sheep, we would hire a ram, called a tup, in the autumn, so that future lambs would not have the same sire. When you have rare breeds, it's not easy to find a male of the right breeding line that is available for tupping, and is not too far away to transport. Our first ram was a four-year-old called Sycamore Iliad. We went off with the trailer to collect him from Carol Colley in Shropshire. Our ewes had been wormed a few weeks previously, so Iliad needed worming before joining them. We thought this would best be done while he was still in the trailer, and, when we got home, I prepared the injection, and waited for Roger to immobilise the ram. Roger opened the tailgate, and squeezed through the wooden doors. Before he could move he was struck hard in the groin by a flying missile: Iliad had rammed him!

Iliad did his job well, but our small flock of ewes had merely whetted his appetite. We had lent the neighbouring field to the Morgans to graze a flock of seventy Clun-cross ewe lambs, which were not being put to the tup that autumn. They were a good size compared to the Hebrideans, large white sheep, larger than Iliad. He liked the look of them. We had anticipated this, and had blocked all the gaps in the hedges with hurdles and erected an additional electric fence. Iliad took a few days deciding which was the best place to do a gargantuan leap, and over he went. We found him, with his new concubines, in the evening when we went to feed the sheep. He was having a rare old time. Our efforts to catch him were pretty futile. We phoned the Morgans, and Richard and Brian came over on the double. It took the four of us to corner the flock, and then Brian did a rugby tackle, and Iliad's jaunt was at an end. He was frog-marched back to our courtyard and confined to jail in the goose shed. We had grown fond of Iliad, and he had become quite tame, but it was time for him to go home. But he had left his calling card – a number of black lambs appeared among the Morgans' large white flock the following spring!

In the autumn of 1995, we hired another ram from Carol Colley: a fine young ram lamb, CleeHills Ebony's Iliad, which she had bred herself. We had a good crop of lambs from him, and were glad to sell the best ram lamb for breeding (the previous year we were forced to cull a magnificent ram lamb for whom we could not find a buyer). Iliad's offspring brought our flock to the required number, and we decided the time had come to buy our own ram.

We found Butts Calum in Ross-on-Wye. He was four years old, rather older than we would have wished to buy in, but he was owned by the farmer who had purchased one of our young rams, and it seemed a good arrangement. We hope that the coming spring will prove that he has done as well as his predecessors.

Iliad had done well, and the lambs were born in April. We brought the ewes into the barn every night when lambing was imminent. They were penned into a central area with hay and water and plenty of fresh straw. Three smaller pens were ready for ewes in labour. We kept each ewe, with her new-born lambs, in one of the small pens for two days, and then they joined the rest of the flock in the field during the day, but were kept separate at night until they were well bonded. Hebrideans are a hardy breed, and good mothers. All lambed easily without our help, although we gave the new-born lambs a rub down and made sure they were suckling the vital colostrum from their dams. They were tiny and wobbly, with dense, curly black coats. An enchanting sight. Their fleeces later became thick and fluffy, and lost their perm!

Although I had done a lambing course, Roger also wanted to gain some experience, and in 1995 he went over to the Morgans during the lambing season, at about ten o'clock at night, and sat with whoever was on duty. The ewes that are due to give birth are brought into a large shed, where separate pens are prepared for the new lambs and their dams. He learned how to look for the signs that a ewe is going into labour; how to help her if she is in difficulty; and how to revive a lamb if it appears to be weak. The lambs were born amongst the flock in the shed, but immediately after birth they were penned up with their mothers, and checks made to ensure that they had started to suckle. If they are all left together, the lambs often get lost and end up as orphans.

Last year Roger again walked across the fields to the Morgans on several nights, and one evening, when Richard was on duty, they talked until about midnight, when Richard decided to go to bed. Roger said he would watch for another couple of hours, and was preparing to leave at about two o'clock when he noticed that one of the ewes was rather restless: standing up; lying down; turning in circles; pawing the ground; and trying to stand away from the other ewes. These are the signs that she is in labour. After fifteen or twenty minutes Roger went over to her quietly, to take a closer look. When he managed to get a clear view of her rear end, his heart missed a beat. The lamb's head was already sticking out, but he couldn't see any feet or legs. Correctly, the front feet and legs should emerge first, followed by the head. If the head comes out first so that the front legs are swept backwards, the shoulders often have difficulty getting through the pelvic gap, and the ewe can get into trouble. The procedure, which Roger had watched Brian and Richard do several times, was to push the head back into the womb, pull the legs slowly forward, and then pull on them gently to encourage a normal birth.

Suddenly, the responsibility of the situation confronted Roger. He didn't want to wake the whole household, but couldn't remember where Richard's bedroom was situated – he decided to try to deliver the lamb.

He had difficulty getting near the ewe, but finally managed to grab hold of some wool on her back. She was much bigger and stronger than our own Hebridean sheep and struggled hard, but he hung on, and eventually managed to hold her still, one arm around her neck and the other holding the wool on her rump. Still holding her round the neck, he reached underneath her with his other hand, got hold of her rear inside leg, and, without much difficulty, pulled it off the ground so that the ewe rolled onto her side. He now knelt behind her back, put one knee on her side just behind her front shoulders to hold her securely down, and released both his hands. The other sheep had scattered during the commotion, but now all was quiet again. They stood in a circle about 10 feet away, watching suspiciously.

Roger now found that one foot had emerged alongside the head. This was not a combination he had been involved with, so he wasn't sure whether the lamb should be pushed back into the womb or not. He pulled the foot gently and it came forward easily until the whole leg was protruding alongside the head. He didn't have disinfectant or elbow-length rubber gloves to attempt pushing the lamb back into the womb, so he thought he would try pulling the lamb out before he gave up and called for help.

He pushed his fingers into the neck of the vulva, spread them around behind the head of the lamb, and pulled gently but firmly. Nothing happened, so he slowly increased the force until, just as he thought he might cause some injury to the lamb or the ewe, the lamb started to come out. At first he had to maintain a strong pull, but suddenly the lamb shot out and lay on the ground behind the ewe, covered in blood and mucus. Roger cleaned the mucus from its face, and was about to tickle its nostrils with a piece of straw, when he saw that the lamb was breathing vigorously.

After a few minutes, he released the ewe from under him, picked up the lamb, and, holding it under the ewe's nose, walked backwards towards one of the pens. The ewe followed him in, and he placed the lamb gently on the straw and closed the pen behind them. He'd delivered his first lamb.

It's important that, like any animal, the lamb suckles in the first few hours to make sure it gets colostrum. The lamb didn't suckle immediately, but then Roger realised that a second lamb was being born. Shortly afterwards, with lots of encouragement through licking and pushing from their mum, the two lambs were drinking their first colostrum.

Roger only got two hours sleep that night, but after breakfast he wanted to go over to the Morgans' straight away to see if the lamb he had delivered was all right. The family were all at breakfast, and he blurted out his story. Brian was the first to see how important it was to Roger.

"Let's go and have a look at them," he said.

They went to the lambing shed, and there were Roger's lambs, full of beans, worrying their Mum constantly for milk, their tails wagging furiously until the teat was found. Another special moment.

In 1996, Theresa had a stillborn lamb in one of our own lambing pens inside the barn. I arrived on the scene soon after his delivery: although the lamb was still warm, he was not breathing. I tried to resuscitate him for about ten minutes, whirling him around, rubbing his heart, giving him artificial respiration and mouth to mouth resuscitation, but he did not respond. His mother's udder soon began to look uncomfortably full, so we thought we would ask the Morgans if they had an orphan lamb that needed a parent. "Of course," said Richard, "come over, and bring the dead lamb with you."

One of the best methods of getting a ewe to adopt a strange lamb is to put the coat of her dead baby onto the new lamb, who has to wear it for up to two weeks, until the ewe has accepted the changeling.

Roger took the dead lamb over to the Morgans',

and, when he arrived, Margaret took him to the pen in the barn where she looked after the orphan lambs which she has to bottle feed several times a day. The lamb she selected was a lot bigger than our dead one, partly because it was already about a week old, but mainly because it was a Suffolk/Mule-cross, an altogether larger animal than a hill sheep.

Meanwhile, Lee had placed our dead lamb on the granary steps, and was starting to skin it with a very sharp knife. He remarked on the dense, curly black coat, much thicker than the coats of lowland sheep. He slit the skin down the inside of the legs and up the belly from the 'nave to the chops', then he deftly separated the skin from the body, cutting across the tail and behind the ears. It took him only a few minutes.

"Have you done this before, Lee?" Roger asked.

"Once or twice," he answered with a twinkle in his eye.

Lee was born on his farm and has lived there all his life. He worked with horses in his youth before the tractors took over and the wonderful draught horses were slaughtered in their thousands across the country.

Richard and Brian work very hard without any help on their large farm. There's always a long list of jobs to be done, and during the peak times of lambing and harvesting they work night and day to get the job done, but I suspect it was a much harder life before mechanisation and the CAP (Common Agricultural Policy). Lee told me that during lambing one year, when he couldn't get any help and Margaret was ill, he didn't take his boots off from Monday to Friday – that was when the ewes were lambing outside, and not in the comparative comfort of a large shed.

We now had a little black woolly coat for our orphan white lamb. Lee cut a small hole in the skin at the end of each leg, and we pulled the orphan's legs through the holes and tied a piece of string to hold it round its neck. It wasn't a Saville Row fit, but it would remain on him long enough to do the job.

We called the adopted lamb Morgan! Theresa accepted him from the start, and became the best and most protective mother in the flock. After about a week, Morgan's coat began to smell. Theresa seemed to love him all the more, but the rest of the flock gave them a wide berth. We would have liked to give him a wide berth as well, but we were still bringing him in every night.

"Can't we take the coat off yet?" we asked Lee.

"Just a bit longer, to be on the safe side."

After another week we could bear it no longer, and the bond between Theresa and Morgan seemed very strong, so we cut the offending garment off. All continued to go well, and Morgan grew in leaps and bounds. He soon grew bigger than his mother. He was very ugly, with a roman nose, a long tail, and large masculine appendages. When he suckled he would have to kneel down in order to get his head in a comfortable position, and would then proceed to wham poor Theresa in the udder to get her milk flowing. He rammed her so hard that she was lifted right off her feet – but she still loved him! We were pretty fond of him as well, but by the autumn we were running the risk of having some white lambs the following spring, so sadly, he had to go. But we had his skin made into a rug, as a reminder of the whole event, and Morgan lives on, very handsomely.

The sheep skins are normally claimed by the butcher when the sheep are slaughtered, but you can buy the skin back from him and have it tanned. We did this with Morgan, because he was special, and also with Compost, because he was the first, but we have also had several more of our Hebridean skins tanned and made into rugs, to give away as presents. There are very few people left nowadays who have this skill, and are prepared to provide a private service. Most of the skins go off in bulk from the abattoir to the factory, where they are converted for various purposes. We were fortunate to find a lady near Hereford who has done the most beautiful job on all our skins. The skins have to be taken to her straight from the abattoir, and she salts them immediately, to preserve them, before starting the tanning process which takes several weeks. Her sitting room is piled high with the most amazing variety of finished skins of all shapes and colours.

Sheep that are not slaughtered have to be shorn every summer, although you can in fact leave hill sheep until their fleeces gradually fall off, but they look extremely moth-eaten meanwhile. The Wool Board will buy the fleeces, and this is obligatory, except in the case of rare breeds whose wool you can sell privately to spinners. If you can find a private market, you will get a better price for the wool.

The first summer that we had the sheep, Brian and Richard came and sheared them for us with portable electric clippers. The sheep were still very wild at this stage, and they were not much better at catching them than we were – except they were a lot faster, and very good at rugby tackles! Once the sheep had been imprisoned in the barn, we were extremely impressed by the ease with which the boys could hold as many as three sheep upright at a time, grasping them by the forelegs. The fleece has to be shorn in one piece, in a certain sequence of cutting, and then rolled correctly into a ball, with the clean side inwards. The inside of the fleece is amazingly soft and clean, and penalties are subtracted by the Wool Board for any dirt, foreign objects such as brambles or straw, or nicks in the fleece. The sheep should not be nicked either, and the wound must be dressed immediately if this happens. Richard and Brian have about four hundred sheep of their own to shear, so our little flock didn't take them long, but it makes a long day just that much longer for them, and we determined to do it ourselves in future.

I was getting quite handy with the hand shears, or dagging shears, that are used for trimming the sheep's hindquarters before tupping and lambing, and as this was the method used in the old days, we thought we would like to try it on our sheep. When I was doing my equestrian course at Holme Lacey College of Agriculture, I had met a champion shearer called David Williams who was the instructor on a shearing course at the time. We got in touch with him, and he agreed to come and give us some instruction, as the process is quite complicated. This instruction was invaluable, but, after one demonstration, he left us to it and went to chat to Richard who had arrived to see the fun! Holding the sheep is hard work, and it is Roger who has ended up doing most of the shearing. It takes us a long time, and is backbreaking, but after seeing a demonstration of hand shearing at the Royal Welsh Fair, we make it a bit easier by sitting the sheep on the old pig bench. We concluded that the secret of shearing is keeping the sheep still whilst both your hands are occupied, one holding the shears and the other keeping the skin flat so there is less chance of cutting the sheep. In principle, having snipped off the loose wool on the chest and belly, you work down one side from head to tail, snipping in tight rows from the chest to the backbone. To keep the sheep still, you hold her very close to your body with your arms and elbows, being careful that her horns don't catch you in the face. Roger took about twenty to thirty minutes for each sheep and managed to keep all the fleeces in one piece, but the sheep he had shorn looked a bit bumpy!

The sheep look very naked and forlorn immediately after being sheared, and the lambs (who are not shorn the first year) have trouble identifying their mamas. There is always a lot of noise in the fields at shearing time, as the lambs run around trying to make out which one of these naked animals is Mum – "Baaaaaa, baaaaa, baaaaa. Oh! Thank goodness! This one smells familiar!"

The summer that we first attempted our own shearing was especially busy for us because the sheep contracted orf, and then New Forest disease. Orf is a very painful and highly infectious condition affecting sheep of all ages. It is caused by a virus which enters the skin and causes blisters on the lips, gums and nose, and the lambs then transfer the infection to the teats and udders of the ewes, making it very difficult and painful for both the mother and the hungry lamb. Being a virus, orf does not respond to antibiotics, and little can be done to help by orthodox methods. Orf is also a 'zoonose', that is to say it can be passed from animals to humans, and Roger developed a huge lesion on one of his thumbs. New Forest disease, or infectious keratitis, is a fly-borne infection of the eyes, starting with mild conjunctivitis and progressing to a pustular discharge and then the development of a cloudy film which spreads across the eye, finally turning opaque with ulceration of the cornea, causing blindness – sometimes permanent.

I had by now done a short course on Veterinary Homeopathy at the Worcestershire College of Agriculture. Although this is a massive and complex subject, it is possible to get a working knowledge of the most common problems and their homeopathic remedies, and we have had success with treating mastitis in both the cow and the sheep; increasing and reducing milk flow in the pigs; scour in both pigs and calves; tendonitis in the pigs and horse; coreoptic mange; and allergies. Homeopathic remedies are not only a great deal less expensive, but they are not traumatic for the animals, have no side effects, and are easy to administer.

However, the vet will always play a vital role, as there are many procedures for which homeopathy is not appropriate, such as surgery, difficult births, diagnosis of acute illnesses, and the times when antibiotics are the only remedy.

The orf responded well to the homeopathic remedies, and we managed to contain it before it spread through the flock, but unfortunately I did not have the remedies for New Forest disease until the condition was well advanced. The sheep had had the infection the previous year, and they had responded to antibiotics. We were extremely worried that some of the worst cases might go blind before we could evaluate the success of the homeopathic treatment, and so we bundled the sheep into the trailer and took them to the vet, who had to inject them directly into both upper and lower eyelids. The vet squashed into the trailer full of sheep; Roger immobilised one animal at a time; and the vet then had to insert a needle into the eyelid of the struggling sheep. All our little Hebrideans are horned, and definitely not docile – it was a traumatic and exhausting process. As well as further sorties to the vet with the worst cases, we had to round up the sheep twice a day, catch and hold each one, and treat them with homeopathic drops both by mouth and directly into the eye. This year we are already giving them prophylactic treatment with homeopathic remedies made from diseased tissues or associated organisms from bacteria or viruses, known as nosodes, and pray that we will never have such an ordeal again.

Morgan was the first to contract orf, and consequently we had handled him twice a day for treatment, and he had become very tame. He used to trot into the corner of the paddock, where he was isolated with Theresa, when it was time for his treatment, after which Płatek, Troy, Theresa and Morgan used to stand together and watch us treating the other sheep in the south field. Płatek and Morgan became such good friends that Morgan tried to suckle him – and Płatek certainly didn't discourage it!

I wish our Hebrideans had been as obliging as dear Morgan. He went for meat, and in fact we kept him for our own use, but by now we were beginning to make a name for ourselves with both lamb and pork. Two of our Tamworth porkers won rosettes at the Royal Welsh Winter Carcass Competition, and we have had so many compliments about the quality of our pork that we have made up a publicity flyer for sale purposes.

Although it is very pleasing to have found a market for our produce, we are even more pleased when we sell animals for breeding. One of our boarlets has just gone to a farm park in Ireland for breeding purposes, and another ten female weaners are presently booked elsewhere.

This summer we sold six ten-week-old gilts to a gentleman in Yorkshire. He was taking his daughter back to university in Kidderminster, and so wanted

to make a combined trip. He arrived with a small van, but the journey had taken less time than he anticipated and it was too early to drop his daughter at the university on his way to us as planned. Consequently, the back of the van was full of all the accoutrements that students carry around with them: television; lamps; clothes; boxes; books, etc. We had to squash all these possessions behind a makeshift barrier before the piglets could be settled in the middle in some straw bedding. I would certainly have liked to have been a fly on the wall when the van was unloaded at Kidderminster – was there a riot of pigs in the quadrangle? His daughter was already having nightmares about the ruination of her college life before it had begun!

Well, we harvest our crops and our animals, but we also harvest produce from the animals: meat from the calves, the sheep, the geese, and the hens, milk, milk products, and eggs.

We sell some of the goose eggs, as a goose will lay as many as thirty eggs, but cannot hatch them all. Last summer Babs had already laid sixteen eggs, when we noticed that she did not seem herself, and was sitting quietly in the middle of the courtyard most of the time, and walking very slowly. We decided that if she showed no improvement by late afternoon, we would take her to the vet. At about five o'clock she went slowly into the goose shed and sat beside the coop where she had laid her eggs. We made an appointment with the vet, got the car out, and I went into the goose shed to fetch Babs. As I walked in the door, she began to throw herself around and flap her wings desperately. She was in her death throes, and died in front of my eyes.

We were shocked and incredulous. We wanted to know what had happened, and telephoned the vet to ask if we could bring her in for a post-mortem. I picked her up; she was warm and soft as in life, but her head fell down limply on its long neck.

Babs had died from peritonitis, caused by an impacted egg. The egg had gone into the peritoneal cavity, where it had set up an acute infection. She would have been in considerable pain, but it is unlikely that we could have saved her even if we had taken action when she first showed any unusual behaviour. Egg impaction is rare in geese, but more common in hens. They say you can sometimes save a hen by holding her over a bucket of boiling water.

Babs and Boris were the first farm animals we had bought, and we felt a great sense of loss. Boris was inconsolable, and sat in a corner with his head under his wing. Geese mate for life, and can pine away if they lose their mate, so we started telephoning to try to find a replacement. It was the wrong time of the year to find a goose, as last year's goslings had already been disposed of, and the adult geese were in lay. Margaret Morgan offered to give us her old white goose, and they brought her over in a sack. Boris came to life – but only to drive her away! We put them together for the night, and after twenty-four hours he accepted the old goose; so he had at least come out of his decline. Michael Roberts of The Domestic Fowl Trust agreed to help me out by selling me one of his laying Brecon Buff geese, as I had sold him some Brecon Buffs the previous year when his geese had not gone into lay. It was a few days before I could make the journey to collect the new goose, and Boris had by now mated with the old white goose, but when he saw Belinda it was love at first sight, and he turned on the poor white goose once more. We had hoped they would all live in peace, but it was not to be, and

Margaret's generous offering was returned – they had thought she was no longer fertile, but she laid four eggs the following Spring!

Since Roger first milked Jonquil in March 1995, we have only had to buy milk for the eight-week resting period before the calf is due. We're thinking of keeping a second cow so that we can bridge this gap (Jonnie is in calf presently with a pure Jersey, in the hope that it will be a heifer after having two bull calves). We give the surplus skimmed milk to the pigs. This is an even more important reason to have a second cow, because at present there isn't enough milk to supplement the inadequate supply of protein from the crops.

We skim off the cream every day, about 15 per cent of the milk. Every few weeks, when we've accumulated 8 litres of cream, Roger makes butter – so we haven't bought any cream or butter either. I make yoghurt from the skimmed milk, and Roger has just started making soft cheese regularly. Hard cheese takes more time and patience (and more milk) but we'll get round to that eventually.

The other produce we are beginning to harvest are the fruits of our vegetable garden and greenhouse.

We bought a second-hand greenhouse, which we had to dismantle *in situ* and reassemble at Upper Bridge Court. It remained stored for nearly a year before we had time to erect it. Walter then came and laid the foundations for us, and Roger had to try to remember how it all fitted together. By then it was a little late to plant tomatoes, but as I had never had a greenhouse before I was determined to have a go. We had a bumper crop – about a month later than everyone else! The heating is not yet connected to the greenhouse, so it has not really been used over the winter, but I shall soon be planting some vegetable seeds in its shelter, to get them off to an early start.

With the help of our gardener, Mark Thomas, who comes in one morning a week, I now have twelve beds prepared in the vegetable garden, and four more are planned. Each bed has an area of 9 square metres. In 1996 (my first year in the vegetable garden), we had our own herbs, potatoes, cabbage, carrots, mange-tout, peas, beans, onions, shallots, parsley, spinach, courgettes, broccoli, and sprouts. There is no question but that everything tasted very fresh and sweet. This year we will have more of everything, and I will start asparagus in May – although this will take at least three years before we can sample it. We've also planted soft fruits: black currants, red currants, white currants, loganberries, tayberries, raspberries and gooseberries. As with most things we are doing here, we have had no previous experience, and so I am learning as I go – with invaluable advice from Walter and Heather, whose vegetable plot is a real show-piece.

In 1996 Mark also planted our small orchard of local fruit trees, mostly old varieties of apple. This is in a sheltered area behind the barn – the impassable piece that Tallulah and Tess first reclaimed from the weeds and scrub. Roger and Troy then harrowed it several times, and Roger sowed fresh grass with his seed fiddle. We won't have many apples for a few years yet, but the orchard already looks a picture.

When we had finished it, and the grass had been mown for the first time, Roger and I leaned on the new surrounding fence (Troy beside us looking longingly at the juicy young grass), and gazed at it admiringly. "What we need is a beehive," I said.

I soon discovered that there is more to keeping bees than just buying a hive and sticking some bees in it. I telephoned the local beekeepers' association, and they advised me to do a bee-keeping course first. These are held in early spring, and I was now too late to get instruction.

"Just as well," I thought. "I wouldn't have time at the moment anyway."

But fate again stepped in. Some very good friends were visiting us, and we were sitting on the porch looking across the meadow, when suddenly the air was filled with a loud humming, almost like a small aircraft, and then a black cloud floated low across the field. It was a swarm of bees. None of us had ever seen one before, and we watched in fascination, thinking it would soon pass out of sight. But it stopped almost directly in front of us, hanging in the air like a huge black sphere, and then hovering over a blackthorn tree, before eventually forming a tight cluster, the size of a rugby ball, on one of its branches. I walked over to get a better look – although keeping a respectful distance away. The glistening black ball was in constant motion, the bees ever changing their position within the cluster to relieve the bees clinging on to the branch, from whom the rest of the bees were hanging. I was worried that Troy might disturb them, and get stung, so I brought him into the stable.

A few days previously I had seen an advertisement for a hive, and I telephoned to see if I could buy the hive and get some help with the swarm. Pam and Bob Mendy came over in the early evening. They lent me some protective clothing so that I could watch what they were doing, and after setting up the hive in a suitable position in the orchard, they turned their attentions to the swarm. I was amazed that they handled the bees without gloves, Bob actually stroking the cluster with his bare hands before, with a sharp rap, they dropped the living ball into a sack and quickly closed the neck. The bees were then safely transferred to their new home. Everything was done very quietly and gently. They told me that some more bees, who were still out foraging, would come and collect in the same spot, and I would have to repeat the procedure the following day. My heart sank.

I managed to transfer the rest of the bees safely, but I did get stung on the wrist, as I hadn't yet got proper equipment and was wearing rubber gloves. I had a severe reaction, and was in considerable pain for several days, even though I had medical treatment. I got enough advice from Pam and Bob to enable me to look after the bees during the summer, but I didn't want to attempt to remove honey until I had been on a course of instruction. The bees are now tucked up for the winter, and I hope I can extract an autumn honey harvest next year.

Mañana

When Earth's last picture is painted, and
the tubes are twisted and dried,
When the oldest colours have faded, and
the youngest critic has died,
We shall rest, and, faith, we shall need it –
lie down for an aeon or two,
Till the Master of All Good Workmen shall
put us to work anew.

Rudyard Kipling

The truth is, we came to Upper Bridge Court to retire. Well, that was our original intention when we decided to move out of London. We were going to find a pretty house in a village, with a tennis club, and do all sorts of things we had had no time to do until now. We would often go to London to the opera and the theatre. Oh yes! and travel to faraway places we had never seen.

Now different things seem important, different things give us pleasure. We still love the theatre, and go to Cardiff to the opera and the theatre, but I look back with disbelief at the Meriel Brooke who was obsessed with acting, yearned for it, lived for it. Yet I have no regrets. I got huge satisfaction from a job well done, from passing on some of what I had learnt to others and seeing them evolve. Roger had always enjoyed what he was doing, and always believed he could master anything he tackled. That life and those battles have made it possible to get such satisfaction from what we are doing now.

We have had to learn the hard way, and, of course, we are still learning, and always will be, but it is very gratifying that people sometimes ask us for advice; it is very satisfying when we are told that our produce is good; it was a wonderful bonus when we received the listed buildings grant for the house and out-buildings; and now we have just heard that we have been accepted into the coveted MAFF Countryside Stewardship scheme. This means that the way we are running the farm has been considered worthy of a financial subsidy for a ten-year plan to improve the hedges, fences, and walls. All these factors have given us new energy and enthusiasm for what we are doing.

We sometimes wish that we had started this way of life sooner, so that we would have had more time to learn, more strength to carry out what we do, and more time to enjoy it all. But, at the same time, we wouldn't have been ready to start sooner, wouldn't have wanted to then. We had to go through our development in different ways, before we were ready to join forces and start something completely different.

At present we are reaching the pinnacle of our

work load. Major jobs on the house are still to be done, as well as major jobs on the farm and in the vegetable garden. There is still much to learn about animal husbandry, and that will be a continuous process. But soon we will finish the big one-off jobs that had to be done at the beginning, and will have more time for daily life. Yes, we will always be busy, but these are the days that we don't want to end; our delight is in living them. We believe that we are indeed privileged to have been given this opportunity to care for these wonderful animals.

Sometime in the distant future we will have to begin to think about having fewer animals, fewer crops. Perhaps we will eventually lease the fields and reduce the vegetable garden. Perhaps one of us will be here for longer, but one thing we know for sure, we will never leave Upper Bridge Court.

We were having lunch a few days ago, and Lesley and little Florek were with us.

"Look," said Florek. "A rainbow in the room!"

The sunlight had reflected off a glass prism on the mirror and a rainbow appeared to shine onto the table.

"Catch it in your hands!" I said.

We all cupped our hands and held them in the coloured light, and the rainbow spilled into and over them.